JACK & JAMIE
GO TO WAR

JACK ROBINSON
JACK & JAMIE
GO TO WAR

◁◁◁GMP▷▷▷

First published in March 1988
by GMP Publishers Ltd, P O Box 247, London N15 6RW, UK
telephone (01) 800 5861
telex 94013925 GMPPP G

Distributed in North America by
Alyson Publications Inc.,
40 Plympton Street, Boston, MA 02118, USA
telephone: (617) 542 5679

British Library Cataloguing in Publication Data

Robinson, Jack
  Jack and Jamie go to War.
  1.Great Britain. Male homosexuality — Personal observations
  I.Title
  306.7'662'0924

ISBN 0-85449-077-9

Made and printed in Great Britain by
The Guernsey Press Co. Ltd., Guernsey, Channel Islands.

Prologue

The sound of silence. The old church bells of St Jude's, St Chrysostom's and St Francis Xavier's should have been ringing in my ears, but the ringing of church bells was now forbidden in the United Kingdom. No bells rang out the eleven solemn chimes, but the people in the city knew it was exactly 11 a.m. Children stopped their street games and stood like statues, shabby-looking workmen removed their two-bob flat caps, gentlemen took off their trilby hats, and busy housewives stood to attention like soldiers.

The city came to a standstill and nothing moved for two whole minutes: it was November 11th.

A schoolboy, one foot on the pavement's edge and the other on his bicycle pedal, looked questioningly into the eyes of the traffic patrolman on duty at the busy city crossroads. The bobby nodded his head. The boy rang his bell, moved off and brought the world back to life.

'This is my home town,' I said to the guy at my side. 'What a fuckin' dump! I hope the bleedin' Germans burn it to the ground. Maybe they'll build some decent houses and parks for the kids to play in.'

'There won't be any kids left,' replied my companion. 'There'll be fuck all left if this lot keeps up.'

We marched into the railway station at Lime Street and found it a shambles; broken glass and rubble all over the place. A small cardboard sign directed us to the railway transport officers' room, so we walked right in.

'Yes?' snapped a middle-aged RTO. 'What is it, corporal? What the hell do you want?'

'Three German prisoners,' I replied, throwing the old major a smart salute. We're the escort from Chester Castle, sir.'

'Right,' said the silly old fool as he examined my papers. 'Sign here. You'll find them under guard on platform two, and keep the bladdy blinds drawn. If the civilians see the buggers, you'll have a bladdy riot on your hands.'

Two red-capped military policemen stood guard outside a

first-class carriage. 'This must be it,' remarked my companion. His name was Sanders but I called him Sandy.

The red caps were glad to see us, checked out the documents we carried and let us board the train. We found ourselves inside a first-class sleeper. Two German flying officers occupied one small compartment, and a pyjama-clad boy lay stretched out on a hospital blanket in the other.

One officer had jet black hair, a few days' growth of beard on his handsome face and a sling around his shoulder supporting a plaster-cast arm. I couldn't make a guess at his age but knew he was under forty. His companion was much younger, blond as the beautiful Jean Harlowe, well fed and husky as a big brown bear. One leg in plaster of Paris, trouser leg slit to the thigh, he leaned on a crutch and winked at me through the corridor window.

'I don't think we'll have much trouble with these poor bastards,' said Sandy, 'but it's gonna be fuckin' boring standing here all day long.'

'Never mind,' I replied as the train moved off. 'We'll enjoy ourselves in Somerset. We can take a week getting back if we play our cards right. The GWR only run about one train a day, and bugger all on Sundays.'

The lad on the blanket-covered cot looked tense, nervous and sweaty. His white pyjama jacket, open all the way, showed a blood-stained patch of lint over one breast. The sticking plaster had peeled away and the lad kept trying to fix it to his sweaty brown chest. He seemed very distressed, so I handed my side-arms to Sandy and went into the boy's compartment. He looked scared as I approached him, picked up a towel to wipe the perspiration from his chest and settled him down on the pillow. He was beautiful, I smiled and felt like kissing him.

'How many years have you?' asked the lovely boy in English.

'You mean, how old am I?'

'Yes,' he replied. 'I have eighteen years.'

'I'm nineteen,' I said soothingly, stroking his soft blond hair and looking affectionately into his clear blue eyes.

'My name is Christian,' said the youngster. 'What will your people do to me?'

'They'll do you no harm,' I assured him. 'You're going to a prison camp and you'll be among your own people.'

Christian smiled as I stroked the soft fair hair from his brow.

'What do they call you?' he asked in a friendly voice.

'Jack. My name is Jack,' I whispered. He was one of my own kind and I knew it.

He fidgeted with the loose sticking plaster but it just peeled away again, so I rubbed the perspiration from his chest, struck a match and held it to the strip of plaster for a second.

'Try it now,' I said gently. The plaster held firm and Christian smiled up at me, his bright blue eyes full of pleasure.

'You have much kindness,' he said shyly. Our fingers touched and we knew for sure.

The train reached Crewe Junction, where a couple of shunters hitched us to an old GWR rattler for the journey into the West Country. There had been 250 separate railway companies at one time, but now there were only four and the Great Western was the worst; the train stopped at every little station along the line.

I had to let him know I cared, so I reached out a hand. 'Sit up,' I asked, 'and let me make you comfortable.'

Christian took my hand and I raised him carefully, sensitive messages of affection running through our skin.

'Would you like to be with your friends?' I enquired pleasantly. 'They're only next door.'

'We bomb your cities and yet you show me kindness,' he said shyly.

'Perhaps, Christian,' I replied, 'perhaps if we'd met before the war, we might have been friends.'

Perspiration streamed down his handsome face, over his freckled nose and onto the blood-stained dressing.

'Do you want to lie down,' I asked, drying his face with a towel, putting a hospital gown across his shoulders and almost trying to smother the boy with love.

'I'm fine,' answered the fair-haired boy, 'but I would like to be with my comrades.'

Sandy was bored to death in the corridor. 'Wheel the two Gerries in with the kid,' I said, 'and then we can take turns in the empty sleeper. One of us can sit in with them. They're harmless enough.' Sandy passed my belt and side-arms, shooed the officers into the lad's compartment and settled down in the empty sleeper.

'Don't fall to fuckin' sleep' were my parting words.

'I won't,' Sandy assured me and placed his dirty great hob-nailed boots on the velvet-covered seat.

Young Christian bucked up when he saw his friends. They spoke no English but showed their gratitude by offering me a cigarette.

'No thanks,' I replied, refusing these donations from the International Red Cross. 'You'll need all the fags you can get where you're going.'

The boy translated my words but it didn't seem to matter. We understood each other perfectly, language barrier or not. The guy with his arm in a sling fished out a pack of playing-cards from his tunic, waved them in my face and smiled.

'Go ahead,' I signalled. 'Do whatever you like. It's a long journey.'

They settled down to play pontoon and I smiled when young Christian drew two aces, split his hand and went for the double just as I would have done. I think it was the simple card game that made me realise they were no different from us.

Sandy appeared in the corridor, poked his head through the door and said, 'I'm hungry. Can we grab a pork pie and a beer at the next stop?'

The prisoners looked up at the word 'beer', offering us some German money, an expensive watch and a hopeful expression. I was actually jealous of them because they'd seen action, and could picture the handsome captain dragging the wounded Christian from the wrecked aircraft, saving the boy's life and receiving his undying gratitude. It was something I needed and seemed the highest pinnacle of love.

The old rattler stopped at a place with a blacked-out name, brown paint, smelly urinals and a tiny buffet bar. I leapt out onto the stone-flagged platform. 'Keep the carriage locked and your fuckin' eyes open,' I shouted through the door. 'I'm gonna grab a bite to eat.'

A real West Country girl stood behind the bar — rosy cheeks, enormous breasts and soft brown hair wrapped up in a turban.

'Let us have a case of light ale?' I asked rapidly. 'I don't have much time.'

'You can't have a whole crate,' replied the surprised girl as if it was something unusual. 'You can have a couple of bottles.'

'They're not for me,' I explained. 'I've got wounded men on the train and they need a drink.'

'Give him a crate of pale ale,' said the white-shirted manager.

'I'll pay,' chipped in an old geezer propping up the bar. 'How much?'

'That'll be nine shillings,' replied the girl with the big tits.

'Many thanks,' said I, picking up a couple of pork pies. 'How much for the grub?'

'A bob,' she said with a smile on her rosy cheeks.

The old geezer gave her a ten-shilling note. 'That makes it square,' he said. 'Better get a move on, son. The train's pulling out.'

'Fuckin' luvly!' enthused my mate when he saw the beer. 'We'll be pissed before we reach Somerset.'

'Catch!' I shouted, throwing him a pork pie. 'We can drink our stupid heads off after we've delivered these guys. Grab a beer. The others are for the Gerries.'

The day seemed like it would never end, but the prisoners didn't seem to care. They drank and sang about their homeland, as only the Germans and the men of Wales can do so sincerely.

'Shepton Mallet,' remarked Sandy. 'Somerton coming up. We're getting off shortly, thank Christ.'

He took the uniformed airmen back to their original compartment and left me with the lonely beer bottles, Christian and the stale smell of tobacco smoke.

'Do you feel better?' I asked.

'Excellent!' replied the boy, settling down on his bunk.

We held hands and I kissed him lightly on the forehead. Christian smiled, squeezed my hand and kissed me on the lips.

'The war won't last forever,' I said soothingly. 'Don't worry. You'll be at home with your family one of these days. Take care of yourself, Christian. They'll treat you alright at the prison camp.'

An army lorry and a miserable old sergeant from a territorial regiment greeted us at the station. The end of the line . . .

'I'll take the bastards now!' shouted the old terrier. 'Bastards! If I had my way, I'd shoot the fuckin' lot of them.' He wanted my signature on a silly scrap of paper but I refused. However, his men climbed aboard the train.

'You can't take the lad in the dressing-gown,' I informed them. 'I'm supposed to hand him over to the RAMC. He's a hospital case.'

A smart young corporal from the Medical Corps strode down the platform.

'Hallo there!' I greeted him. 'I think I've got a patient for you. He's only a kid and he's a bit nervous.'

'A chest wound?'

'That's the one. Look after him, corporal. That fuckin' old sergeant is acting potty. I wouldn't trust him.'

'He'll be alright with me,' replied the friendly medic as he helped young Christian into a Red Cross car, 'but he shouldn't have travelled with a wound like that.'

The boy saluted me. 'Goodbye, Jack,' he murmured softly. 'Auf Wiedersehen!'

'So long, Christian!' I threw him a sloppy salute and turned my back. It all seemed so bloody stupid, but I loved it . . .

Sandy packed the side-arms in a kit bag and we walked into a nearby inn where we drank a couple of glasses of scrumpy with the locals and booked a room for the night.

It was almost closing time when the innkeeper's wife showed us to our room. I undressed quickly, took a standing bath with the primitive sanitary arrangements available, slipped into a fresh pair of gym knickers and slid between the sheets. Sandy wasn't far behind. He joined me a few minutes later, apple-smelling breath on my shoulders, firm stomach muscles tight against my back.

The innkeeper made the most amazing crashing sounds as he locked up for the night. Aircraft flew in the night sky, engines throbbing, going who knows where? The sound of local drinking men came up from beneath our bedroom window. My friendly bed-mate put his hand on my hip and the sounds faded into insignificance.

He was a quiet, gentle boy really, eighteen years old and smooth as silk about the face. We all spoke rather rough and ready, cursed and swore and acted tough; we had to. I hadn't slept with the handsome young soldier before and for all I knew, he was virgo intacta heterosexual boy.

However, the light hand on my waist made me feel sexy. Soldiers in gym knickers look much different from those in uniform, and of course the warmth of his body made me think about the half-naked creature — thick brown curls, fair-skinned cheeks, smiling eyes and pearly white teeth. His hand dropped lightly onto my shorts, touched the stiff erection and squeezed it gently.

'Mmmmm!' I sighed with pleasure.

His own penis stiffening beneath me, Sandy boldly pulled my knickers down. Naturally enough, I turned to face him, placed my lips on his cheek and my hand on his lovely bare bottom. He smelled fragrant and masculine. We pulled close without a word being spoken and struggled out of the tight little knickers. Sandy's fingers held my bottom firm and we moved together like excited boys do at times like this.

I kissed him very lightly on the lips and he spoke. 'I never kissed a boy before.'

'Have you kissed a girl?' I asked.

'No,' replied the lovely young soldier. The only person I've ever kissed is my mother, but I saw you kissing the German boy. Do you like kissing boys?'

'Very much,' I answered truthfully.

We moved together a little faster, exchanging feather-light kisses and clinging tight as the magic fluid shot from us.

That's what I liked about the War: anything could happen, and I wondered what would happen next . . .

JACK & JAMIE
GO TO WAR

1. Sing For Your Supper

There was no military parade to see me off, no glittering band, no thundering hooves and handsome lads, nothing. It was all over. I was on my way back to Liverpool where the bugs wear clogs. No regrets. No teardrops on my drum. I could cry another day. It had all been so wonderful and exciting, but sixteen years had seemed a long time to serve. I was still only fifteen and had the whole wide world in my arms.

Discharge papers folded neatly in the breast pocket of a new serge suit, I stepped aboard the puffing billy and waved goodbye to the Boys' Battery at Woolwich. Things had worked out by themselves. A sore throat had put me in hospital and tonsilitis had been diagnosed.

'We have to remove your tonsils and adenoids,' said the medical officer, 'and we need your parents' permission to operate.'

The matron gave me some documents. 'Send these home and get them signed,' she said.

I sent them off. 'Please don't sign,' I wrote. 'I don't want an operation. There's nothing wrong with me.'

Fortunately, my mother refused the operation and set the wheels in motion for my army discharge. Perhaps it was all for the best. Close friends long gone, Toby to the Veterinary Corps, Chesty . . . tears fell when he came to mind. Service as a boy soldier had given me a little taste of life and left me with an appetite for more. Maybe I could join the Merchant Marine, get a berth as a cabin boy and sail the seas like my grandfather and his father.

Big Jack, my great-grandfather, had sailed out of Cardiff Bay in the slave ships. The tales I'd heard at my granddad's knee were so romantic and exciting. Perhaps I could go west and become a cowboy like my uncle Charlie. Dreams flying around in my head . . .

'Lime Street Station!'

I was back among the street cries of Liverpool, romantic dreams swept away, brushed into the gutters with the horseshit of Merseyside. Stephenson's rocket was still there. Nothing had changed.

'Last City *Echo*!'

'Tuppence a bunch the daffs!'

'Ee ar lad! Luvly coconuts a penny each!'

'A penny! I bet there's no bleedin' milk in 'em!'

'Cheeky bugger! Two a penny lemons!'

My family had moved because they couldn't pay the rent. The old man was sick but he'd managed to settle them into some rooms above a shop in Rocky Lane. I was so ashamed of my own failure, I couldn't even show my nose in the old neighbourhood. What had happened to the adventurous young soldier?

My schoolfriend, Eggy, lived with his uncle Paul. I wanted to call and see them but couldn't find the courage. Another day perhaps.

Eddie, my old and wonderful friend, would always care. Unfortunately, I discovered, he had another boy by this time, a sweet-faced lad of twelve, pretty as a picture, eyes of ocean blue. I fell for him, wanted him. I was growing fast and needed a boy of my own. When the time came, when I was a little less self-conscious, I'd try and face Eddie.

Life was reasonably good, however: a few friends here and there and some interesting moments in the cinemas. There was always a sexy young lad about, someone like myself who understood my ways and sensitive thoughts. We played at kneesy in the darkness of the theatre. Kneesy sometimes led to another interesting little game called bumsy, but not very often.

The old man got worse, went into hospital and coughed his life away. I saw him on his last night. He reached for me, took my hand, kissed my cheek and died. No tears escaped from my blue eyes. His one-legged pal was crying, but I couldn't shed a tear. The family wept at his funeral. Perhaps I wasn't much good.

Still seeking the important boy in my life, I was also desperately searching for a job, with time just ticking along. Queues along the waterfront. Riveters building mighty ships at Cammel Laird's, white-hot rivets glowing, spinning, flying through the salty air and landing neatly in the rivet boy's catching cone. He holds the sparkling steel in place. An unseen worker drives it home and flattens the metal into the ship's plate. A boy screams, 'Heads up!' A flying missile lands in the rivet lad's cone, and he moves on a few inches.

How many rivets make a ship? How many steel plates feel the rivet gun's pound? How much valuable time?

Jazz bands roam the stony roads, ukeleles, strumming banjos, men in funny hats and fancy dress. Children at the pavement's edge, bare feet in the dirty gutter, lips moving silently, mouthing the chorus of the street singer, joining in his search for daily bread.

Liverpool, Liverpool! Dirty old town, I know I love you dearly, but why must you sing for your supper?

Back to Rocky Lane, a bag of chips and my little world of make believe in the cinema. Perhaps there was no luck today but I'll find a ship to faraway! Liverpool, Liverpool! Sing for your bloody supper? I want no part of that.

Duffy was a fine big lad, fifteen years old and bright as a button. He leaned his racing bike against the wall, removed the lamp and walked into the office building.

'Any vacancies?' he asked the receptionist.

'Yes.'

'Eh?'

'Yes,' repeated the young lady. 'We're taking lads on. Sit over there.'

He sat beside me. 'Are you waiting for a job?' he asked.

I liked him instantly, something about his cheerful manner, shiny blond hair, smooth with cream and pressed into waves with fingers. His face was strong and square, a handsome boy, wide-set eyes, grey or blue depending on the light that shone. The shirt he wore was spotlessly clean but wet beneath the arms. A bib and brace covered his chest, a greasy garment, shoes brown and scuffed. A big lad, very powerful looking.

He dug me with his elbow. 'Here's the boss. Fuckin' hell. Looka the state of him!'

The works manager came into view. A greasy looking wretch, he was part bald with shiny strands across his yellow pate, dirty fingers, a filthy brown smock and dollops of axle grease on his shoes and smeared over the clipboard in his hands.

'Come with me,' he said in a high-pitched voice and walked ahead.

'My name's Duffy,' said the kid with the waves. 'What's yours?'

'Jack.'

'Looks like we got a job!'

A door opened and we stepped into another world. Fantastic! A nightmare of spinning wheels and dreadful, ear-shattering noise. Long steel driveshafts sprouted from the dirty walls and ceiling. Dynamos screamed and metal screeched, and wheels and wheels and wheels. Huge leather belts linked the driveshafts. Double steel wheels — one to drive, one to run free — pounded and spun at the machines that lined the concrete floor.

There seemed to be hundreds of machines — grease spurting, belts slipping — and white-hot braziers at their sides. Boys in stained bib and brace, yellow skins, dirty hair, filthy fingers and hob-nailed boots. Pounders, stampers, cutters and lathes, filings of brass beneath the feet. Noise! Noise! Unbelievable noise.

The greasy guvnor looked at me and beckoned with his finger.

You have to speak like me,' he said quite clearly. 'Try it!'

I imitated his high-pitched voice and said to Duffy, 'I'm fifteen. How old are you?'

He opened his mouth. What a sight! A double upper lip, double gums, teeth everywhere, More teeth than a shark, two rows on the top and two rows on the bottom!

'Talk through your nose,' said the boss. 'You'll soon get used to it. The first twenty years is the worst.' He stationed us at a hot stamping machine and gave the operating instructions.

Duffy greased the die, then reached with a pair of long pincers into a brazier full of hot brass blanks that stood alongside the machine, removed a red-hot billet and placed it on the sizzling surface of the die. When he removed his long-handled instrument, I pressed the starting lever and set the enormous press in motion. It came down with a mighty crash, squashed the brass billet into the shape of a gas fitting and returned to its original position. My mate levered off the finished work, slung it in a container and shoved another brass billet under the press.

'Swap places every day,' instructed the boss. 'If you get a burn, run it under the cold tap.'

'Where's the tap?' asked the fair-haired lad.'

'In the lavatory.'

'Where's the lavatory?' I enquired but greasy Joe was on his way. Business called.

Each time the noisy tool came down, it tripped a lever that counted the work. Duffy got beneath the machine and examined the trip mechanism.

'We can fiddle this,' he said with a smile, showing those dreadful teeth.

'How?'

'Turn the numbers over. It's like a speedo, a mileometer. Jesus! We can earn a fortune! It's piecework and we get paid for every fitting we turn out.'

'Suppose they count the work?'

'Suppose they don't.'

We could hear each other clearly, but I just hoped that I didn't finish up with a voice like the boss.

Every machine was operated by a wide spinning belt. You could move the leather strap onto freewheel and stop the action but not the belt movement. It spun the twin wheel and carried on working.

Going into freewheel was quite a dangerous performance and led to loss of life and limb. Beware of belts! Do not touch! Leave it to the fitters! warned the notices.

I also saw my first lavatory joke in the brass-stamping factory. It was foul and turned me off my fellow workers on the shop floor.

'Balls!' I said to Duffy. 'I don't want to spend my life in a joint like this.'

'It's a job,' he replied. 'Do you wanna come to the pictures with me tonight?'

'Where do you live?'

'Windsor Road. Where do you live?'

'Rocky Lane.'

'That's just around the corner from me. I'll call for you this evening. There's a smashing picture on at the Majestic.'

Then it was back to the smells of human beings, burning grease and molten brass, and sounds so unfamiliar that I couldn't identify them for a while. The slosh of liquid beneath my feet, a boy in steel-capped boots and tatty boiler suit splashing water from a rusty bucket. His mate slouched behind and swept the filthy mess into puddles of tiny filings, lumpy sawdust and swarf-filled blobs of axle grease.

'Knocking off time,' he said in the high-pitched sing-song of the shop-floor worker. 'Better turn your furnace down.'

Duffy emptied the brazier, switched off the flame and came round to my side of the machine. The power went off. Silence . . . the sound of silence, a strange relief to ears in distress. Hob-nailed boots rang cheerfully on the stone and concrete floor, then suddenly a siren screamed and scared me for a second.

'Let's go!' shouted my cheerful mate. 'Let's get out of this place!'

I didn't know there were so many bicycles in the world. Bikes as far as the eye could see. Flat-capped workers, hatless youths and pretty girls all grabbed their metal steeds and scrambled for a place at the factory gate. Some were stopped and searched by security men, but nobody seemed to object.

Duffy called that evening in a smart grey suit, high-collared military raincoat and polished shoes. He found me wearing an expensive-looking overcoat, powder blue, high tailored collar, a lining of scarlet satin.

'Christ!' he said. 'You look posh. Where did you get the coat?'

'Paddy's market. I work there from time to time. Pick up all kinds of gear. This only cost a few bob.'

'You look like a private eye.'

A handsome pair, we strolled down town. Duffy had started work at fourteen, spent more than a year in a steel-drum factory, carried 56lb sheets of metal for eight hours a day and built himself a body like Samson. I knew instinctively that he wasn't meant for me. However, when we came out of the cinema, he surprised me. 'You look like Errol Flynn,' he said.

'The film star! Humph!' I replied, touching the wavy quiff at the top of my head, face aside, acting it up. 'People say I look like Robert Taylor, the most attractive guy in the world!'

We broke into a fit of laughter and joined the queue outside the chip shop. Greasy chips in the Liverpool *Echo*, cigarette behind the ear, we strolled the city pavements.

'Do it again,' said Duffy.

'Do what?'

'All that funny stuff.'

It didn't seem all that funny to me, but I acted up again and he choked with laughter. There was absolutely nothing there, no girls, no boys, nothing, a sexless lad. I liked him nonetheless. He was my mate, my sidekick and called for me every night of the week. Perhaps he wasn't one of my own kind, but I needed close friends, and none could be better than Duffy.

Piecework or no piecework, we always seemed to get the same weekly wage. 'You only gave me fifteen bob,' I said to the wages clerk. 'It says sixteen on my pay packet.'

She looked at me like I was turd on the pavement. Putting her pencil behind her ear, she explained about the deductions. 'Fourpence for your National Insurance stamp and eightpence for sports facilities.'

'What sports facilities.'

'The playing field.'

'What bloody playing field?'

The factory job didn't last very long. The company completed a few large orders, dismissed the latest recruits to their workforce and put those that remained on short time. There were quite a few business enterprises in the Derby Lane area, however, so Duffy and I searched the industrial estate on our bikes.

'Any vacancies?'

'No. Try the paint works.'

'Any vacancies, sir?'

'Not today, lad. Try the Automatic Telephone Company.'

The Dunlop tyre works, Crawford's biscuit company, the Meccano, anywhere and everywhere . . .

On most afternoons, however, we could be found in the cheaper seats of a cinema. The matinee audience was always the same, no dashing trenchcoats, no latest styles or fashionable wear, but lines and lines of shabby unemployed men, very few girls and a sprinkling of truant schoolboys.

But Dame Fortune smiled on us in Derby Lane and we started work in a radio factory. The foreman looked like a singer named Bing Crosby, so that's what the works called him. Bing showed us to one of the dozens of long tables with flat bench seats beneath glaring neon strips that filled the workshop space. A line of boys sat at one table, a row of girls at the table in front, a line of sweaty lads at the next and so on, separated down the length of the workshop.

If they had been human beings, real boys and lovely girls, it might have been quite pleasant. Unfortunately, they were like pieceworking robots with quick eye movements, flashing fingers and lines of concentration at the forehead.

Smells of static hit the nostril, tiny wisps of smoke stung the eye and sparks flew from a hundred soldering irons. Each worker had a carton of radio components at hand. Number one picked up a metal chassis, inserted a component and passed it down the line. Number two clipped or screwed another part in place and passed the chassis to the next guy. It was almost a complete radio when it reached the end of the bench and was passed to the girls' table for soldering. The young factory girls performed their tasks in much the same way, each one soldering a different part or component. A chargehand counted the finished items and a trolley boy wheeled them off to the inspection room. This went on all day long, with a break for cans of tea and a sandwich at lunchtime, and the odd trip to the lavatory during working hours. Pencilled graffiti covered the walls in the boys' washroom, and scarlet lipstick daubed the wooden doors of the girls' lavatory. Bing timed the youngsters and complained bitterly if they spent more than a couple of minutes there or wasted a few precious moments with a cigarette.

The lads could spare no time for flirting with the girls, and if the pretty things tried to look at the boys they would burn their fingers on the soldering iron. Some of the more stunning young ladies could flutter a long eyelash at Bing and get away with it, but they couldn't get away with Bing. He was only interested in the number of radios produced and the amount of money in his pay packet.

Apart from a few electric shocks, the job wasn't too bad. Unfortunately we got the bullet after a few months. Same old story: too much stock and not enough sales.

'That's enough!' I said to my mate. 'I'm finished. No more factories for me. I'm going to find a ship and get away from all this.'

'I'll come with you,' he said, teeth sparkling — millions of them.

In white shirts and shanghai jeans — dungarees which were

narrow at the knee, bell-bottomed at the ankle and tight about our youthful seats — we stroll the dockland quays and wharves.

The Pier Head: the floating pier pitches and tosses like a ship at sea, straining at its massive mooring, rolling with the tide. Dirty brown waves crash into the buoyancy tanks, floating gangways rise and fall. Salt spray stings the eye, tangy at the lips and tongue.

On to the quayside, past the greying policeman at the dock entrance. We throw him a two-fingered salute and walk on by. We're in! No longer on the floating stage, we search among the tall ships in the harbour: vessels from afar, ancient troopers, cargo boats, ships from sunny Africa, China boats from Birkenhead and passenger liners from America, Canada and Australia.

Chain gangs of white-coated stewards unload the passenger luggage, portmanteaux, bags, metal-bound trunks and battered valises. Smells abound. Coffee beans and coconut and salty waves of grey, sugar cane and palm oil and flotsam in the filthy bay. The distinct odour of hot pitch hits the nasal passage.

'Mmmm!' says my mate. 'I love the smell of tar.'

Ropes and hawsers, coils slippy underfoot.

'Below!' shouts a lopsided stevedore. He has the uneven shoulders of a man who works long hours with a dock-hook, carrying the formidable instrument in a leather trouser-belt and wearing it at the small of his back. One hand is larger than the other. Truly a man who has slung his hook at many crates and bales.

Oranges and lemons pile the wharfside. Rope-bound crates of fruit swing down from the rusty derricks to be trundled away by hand barrow, stacked in square blocks, marked with chalk: Cunard Line, Blue Star, Elder Dempster Shipping Company. Banana boats, floating coffins, lie packed from stem to stern with the unripened green fruits of the West Indies. Who would sail on a banana boat? Bad news!

A white-clad chef, tall starched hat, spotless neckcloth at his throat, waves to us from the rail of a ship.

'D'you need a couple of galley boys, chief?'

'No chance! Try the Shipping Federation.'

'Might as well try the friggin' dole.'

The tide turns and the wind drops. The sun on our backs, we head for home and wend our way up town. Past the Corporation muck yard, the smells from the bins. Flies swarm around the garbage. Stinking dung carts, grey, brown, rusty, lie with their empty shafts pointing to the sky like arms outstretched in despair, derelict, out of business ... unemployed. They shifted three hundred tons of horseshit every day until the automobile came rattling along and put them on the scrap heap.

Meanwhile in dusty Dale Street the labouring man's ballet is under way. The audience lean enchanted against the post-and-rail barrier that lines the pavement's edge, awaiting the curtain's rise; pipe smoking, tobacco chewing, an eager gathering of nosey parkers.

A handsome curtain-raiser flexes his brown-skinned muscles. He swings his pick, breaks into the dirt of the square stone sets and prises them apart. The crowd smile. He takes no bow but swings the gleaming axe again and plays out his opening role, torso sweating, rippling, a tower of strength. His half-naked mate gathers up the stones, piles them at the roadside with his bare hands, playing to the gallery as the traffic rolls by.

A tight-trousered tableau of handsome young labourers set to work at chipping the squares of granite, chisel-shaped hammer blades sending the sparks and masonry flying. A murmur of admiration from the front of the house.

The scene changes. A little burlesque from a young stalwart of the Emerald Isle who holds up a dirty palm and stops the rattling tramcar with one wave. Smiles, murmurs of applause, a little expectant shuffling in the auditorium as the intimate review moves into the closing stages. The crowd thickens.

On stage, the fine young labourers bend their trunks in the most provocative way, set the stones in position and move out of the limelight. Enter the star! A muscular young giant takes centre stage, golden skin agleam with perspiration, head in the clouds, perfect tool in hand, a powerful thing of beauty which he handles carefully, lovingly. This is his moment!

Shiny cord trousers tied above the calf, he swings a mighty, hand-held pile driver and smashes the granite squares into the soft sandstone belly of Liverpool. Applause! Applause! Encore!

Next performance, Brownlow Hill, tomorrow 2 p.m. The main attraction — a massive steamroller, brought from Bolton at great expense, courtesy of Liverpool Corporation road-surfacing department. Come one! Come all!

Duffy has to attend the dole school so his mother can claim benefit. The dole school is like any other place of education but the pupils are unemployed youths who pay no attention to the teachers, smoke, swear and create havoc in the broken-down classrooms of the old-fashioned church schools.

It is not for me. I don't bother with dole but fend for myself and seldom sleep at home. Most of my nights are spent at the house of Annie Jones, a market trader who has known me all my life — a wonderful scouse 'Mary Ellen' with two beautiful daughters who spend their waking moments at the Grafton Rooms, Liverpool's palais de danse. I seldom see them in the daylight hours, but when I do, they are painting their toenails, washing their lovely hair and preparing for another romantic evening on the highly polished surface of the jazz hall. They have a younger brother named Jimmy, a handsome schoolboy who treats me as a member of his family. He is rough, uncouth and sings like an angel at the church of St Francis Xavier.

The house is situated in a downtown building, twenty feet above street level and known as The Buildings. There are no bathrooms. Most of the dwellings are badly furnished and scruffy, but Annie Jones is house proud with a well-furnished home that sparkles like the golden cross she wears at her breast.

The steel-railed landing alongside the dwellings houses the few communal lavatories, one formidable closet to every six families. Young Jimmy and I use the public bath-house nearby, bathe two or three times a week and steal the Corporation towels.

After a while Duffy and I started work in an enormous provisions warehouse near the docks. Open hoist doors lined the fourth floor, the level on which our department was situated. Blocks and tackles and ropes and hooks dangled from every gaping hoist, hanging out over the busy dockland scene below. Each floor was called a high, two high, three high and so on. Four high was fifty feet above the road surface. Flat-capped, white-aproned warehouse porters manned the hoists and worked long hours loading and unloading hundreds of waiting vehicles. Ropes and chains rattled up and down the battered walls to shouts of 'Below!' amd 'Heads up!'

Men on three high cursed and swore at guys on other levels. Busy porters trundled the goods to and fro by hand barrow, stacking, shifting, carrying and packing. Goods arrived from all over the world, every provision in the grocery trade: smoked sides of bacon from Denmark, cases of tea from China, India and Ceylon. Lard in wooden cases, sugar in 2-cwt sacks. Tinned pilchards, salmon, Libby's baked beans and Fray Bentos cases of corned beef. There were pineapple chunks and honey and spice, dried fruits and peppercorns and everything in the giant pantry of Merseyside.

Italian cheeses were so enormous that they had to be turned by mobile block and tackle; but large or small, each one had to be turned daily to allow the mass of compressed curd to mature. The guys who performed this operation were men of steely sinew and rippling muscle, grubby shirts bursting at the seams.

Duffy and I worked at box-making machines in the butter department. They were simple enough to operate. Stacks of wooden ends, sides, bottoms and tops stood alongside the machines. The operators placed the wooden parts in position, pressed a foot pedal and watched the one-inch nails slide down a chute. An automatic hammer drove them into place.

As one person built an open box, completed it and set it on the warehouse floor, another placed it on an escalator belt and sent it to the butter department. The same guy returned with packed boxes of wrapped butter and stacked them by the nailing machine operator. This is where the real work started. Each box weighed 28 lbs, and the guy at the machine had to put lids on them. The nailing action only took a few seconds, which meant the kid at the machine was bending, stretching, handling and stacking 28 lb weights for hours on end.

Muscles appeared like magic and my lanky frame soon filled out. We played catch with cases of butter and stacked them so high that nobody could unstack them. Some of the containers weighed 56 lbs, and we tossed them around like feathers.

From sweet young lad to muscular roughneck in a few short months. The guys were rough and proud, loved to boast of their youthful strength and thought nothing of smashing their stupid heads through the half-inch timber of the butter boxes. Recklessly, we dived through open hoist doors, grabbed a rope and swung out into the polluted air of dockland shouting 'Look out below!'

Lunch was taken in the stockroom, blue-clad bottoms astride a fine cheese from Italy, cans of hot tea all round, games of pontoon and brag in progress. Fights broke out when tempers flared but Duffy and I were never involved in brawls. Perhaps it was my mate's smile. One look at his crazy teeth would frighten the Prince of Darkness himself! I couldn't really understand our relationship — no girls, no boys and no sex. Just me and my shadow.

Eventually we got the sack after a huge box of butter went crashing into the street below and demolished the foreman's second-hand Morris. Butterfingers! There were other little jobs to be found. They came and went, a job here and a job there.

One guy bought a few Chryslers and Oldsmobiles from a salvage collection at the dockside. They had been at the bottom of the Mersey but were absolutely spanking new. He engaged me and Duffy to dry them out, clean them up and give them a coat of Simonize. He was so pleased with our efforts that he kept us on and gave us a job as garage hands.

This was a real step forward into the new world. We learned to drive, borrowed a car and went joy-riding all over Lancashire. When the boss discovered we'd been taking his cars without permission, he took us into his tiny office and gave us our marching orders.

Willing to try our hands at almost anything, we started the next day as steeplejack's mates. Holy Christ!

The morning sun broke through the clouds and glistened on the old grey Mersey. Beautiful seagulls soaring, hovering, swooping gracefully all around. What strange tale had I heard at my grandfather's knee about the old dockside church of St Nicholas? Gone. Lost among the many stories that filled my silly head.

Seeing shadows on the far horizon, I shaded my eyes with flattened palm and saw the fleet arriving: long steel vessels of battleship grey, broad-beamed fighting ships all in line, belching smoke. Then it all came flooding back.

My granddad's yarn, I remembered it well: the old church bells had always rung merrily when the slave ships returned from the West Indies and America, holds bursting with bales of cotton, sugar, Virginia tobacco and other trading goods which they'd exchanged for human beings. 'Down to the harbour!' rang the bells of St Nick's. 'The cotton's coming in!'

'Hey Duffy' I called from the top of St Nick's. 'Let's climb down and join the navy!'

'Suits me,' said handsome Duffy. 'Let's go!'

We were seventeen. I saw the world from the top of St Nick's and heard it calling me.

2. Chester Castle

Duffy led the way into the Royal Navy recruiting office.

'Knock and enter,' read the sign on a polished inner door.

'Here goes!' he said.

All kinds of exciting pictures lined the office walls: the Rock of Gibraltar, the Royal Fleet anchored off Malta, a huge battleship with grey spume and dark green waves washing over the decks, polished 16-inch guns and colourful bunting from stem to stern. An enormous oil painting of 'The Death of Nelson' adorned the far wall, and sitting at a desk beneath its gilt frame was a bearded naval officer who looked like George V.

'Yes?'

'We want to join the navy.'

The bearded officer led us into the medical officer's waiting-room with a line of changing cubicles, little curtained alcoves and highly polished timber everywhere. It seemed I'd been this way before.

We changed into woollen dressing-robes and took our separate seats. Duffy was called first; he came out ten minutes later, face as long as a fiddle, blue rejection slip in his meaty hand.

'What's up?'

'Every fucken' thing! I'm colour blind.'

'Colour blind?'

'Yeah, they gave me a load of bleedin' flags to look at and I made a balls of it. It's no good! They won't have me — the silly bastards talk with flags in the navy.'

'Jesus! Can't they afford a fucken' wireless? Come on, let's go,' I said, climbing into my trousers. 'We'll have to go to Seaforth and try the army.'

'Why Seaforth?'

'I've been in the army once. They've got my particulars in Liverpool and the recruiting sergeant knows me.'

'I thought you wanted to go to sea.'

'Not by myself. Come on. The army's ok.'

'Why did you pack it up?'

'I was only a kid. Anyway, I didn't pack it up. I got thrown out on medical grounds but there's fuck all wrong with me.'

Seaforth Barracks, the home of the King's Liverpool Regiment, was about seven miles out of town. We arrived there in the afternoon, passed the medical and signed up for six months with the supplementary reserve, a special reserve force that took youngsters under the age of eighteen.

'If you like it,' said the husky recruiting sergeant, 'you can sign on for seven years with the colours. If, after six months, you find it's too tough, you can go home to mummy but you'll be called up for active service in the case of national emergency. Understand?'

'No.'

'Never mind. You're in the army now. You'll soon learn.'

We were exactly seventeen and a half; only a few weeks separated our birthdates.

A couple of days later, railway warrants in hand, we boarded a train for Chester and set out for Chester Castle, an ancient granite fortress on the banks of the river Dee. It was the month of August, so my sabre-toothed companion and I were put into August squad, the latest recruiting section of the Cheshire Regiment. August squad consisted of thirty raw recruits; the under eighteens were in the supplementary reserve and the other poor bastards had signed for seven years.

'Name?' called the sergeant-major, pointing his pencil at a cross-eyed lad in ill-fitting army fatigues.

'Jones,' said the boy.'

'Occupation?'

'Unemployed.'

The sergeant-major went down the line of farmer's lads, warehouse porters and more unemployed.

'Name?' he asked me.

'Robinson,' I replied. 'J. Robinson.'

'Occupation?'

'Steeplejack's mate,' I lied. A few kids looked in my direction, but I had my head screwed on and knew what I was doing.

'Name?' the sergeant asked a fair-haired boy.

'Jamie Dunlop,' replied the lad.

'Dunlop will do!' said the irritable sergeant-major.

'Occupation?'

'Scholar,' answered the fair-haired boy.

'That's not an occupation,' said the sergeant-majopr. 'I'll put unemployed.'

'Why not put student or scholar?' asked Jamie. 'I came straight from school and I object to being classed as unemployed. I want to become an officer, and it won't look very good having the word unemployed on my records.'

'Oh Christ,' cursed the sergeant-major. 'There's one in every bloody squad!'

The boy's face went quite red, but the company commander slapped a swagger stick against his rich leather riding boot, making us all jump with fright. 'The boy's right,' he said in a loud voice. 'Put scholar in the column, CSM.'

'Sir!,' screamed the CSM, like all military men do when an officer corrects them.

Jamie, it turned out, was bunking next to me. Two kids came over to the fair-haired boy and one of them dumped the lad's kit on the barrack-room floor. 'You're a snotty little cunt!' he said. 'What makes you think you're better than the rest of us?'

'I don't,' replied the boy. 'I'm new here just like everyone else.'

The two lads pulled his bedding onto the floor.

'Why don't you two fuck off!' I snarled in my nasty Liverpool accent. 'If you fuck about with this kid's gear, we won't pass inspection and that means we won't get out at the weekend, you stoopid bastids.'

I was a big kid for seventeen. My face may have been pretty, but I had good shoulders and fists, and the way I spat out the word 'bastid' always did the trick. Jamie squared up alongside me and the two lads almost apologised. 'He's right!' said one. 'We'd best get sorted out or we won't get out on Saturday.'

That's how it all started. Jamie told me about his life in a small Lancashire mining town, and asked me to join him in the canteen for a coffee. He had those faraway eyes, long-lashed and blue as the Mediterranean sea. I fell in love with the gentle creature the moment we met, but he was so refined and well educated that I thought he wouldn't want anything to do with a kid from the docklands of Liverpool.

'Were you really a steeplejack's mate?' he asked in his wide-eyed innocent way.'

'I've been all kinds of things,' I told him. 'I pissed off from home before I was fourteen, and I knocked about here and there. I'll tell you more when we get to know each other better.'

Jamie studied French, wrote beautiful letters and read books and poetry from morning till night. But he could look after himself, and had the makings of a soldier. I played with myself in my bunk just thinking about him.

Most of the boys were friendly enough and, as our training progressed, little friendships developed and the close-knit barrack-room family began to take shape.

'Take that cigarette from behind your ear,' Jamie chided me. 'It's uncouth. Please don't be offended.'

I didn't mind. I had a few bad habits and was always willing to learn.

'Why don't you read more?' he asked one day.

'Why don't you get in the gym and improve your body?' I answered back.

The morning lessons in the gym were simply training sessions under an instructor, but the voluntary gym session at night was absolutely different; a guy could do exactly as he wished. I was a gym enthusiast and helped my fair-haired friend improve his body. He helped me in other ways, polishing my rough edges and teaching me a few important things about social behaviour. We walked the battlements of Chester Castle arm in arm on our way to breakfast, and marched through the ancient cobbled streets of the city like automatons, arms swinging, eyes to the front and heads held high and proud. We were meant for each other and loved each other's company.

Unfortunately, soldiers in a garrison town like Chester were considered the lowest form of animal life. People treated us like dirt and thought us the scum of the earth. Respectable girls would not be seen dead with a soldier. The only girls available were known as 'barrack rats' and were little more than prostitutes. The first battalion was stationed in India and suffered the indignity of posters at the officers' and gentlemen's clubs proclaiming: 'Dogs and soldiers not allowed.' Jamie and I would belong to the second battalion when we finished training. He knew that we would go to India when the other battalion came home, so he studied Hindi and Tamil. He spent a lot of time reading: the King's Regulations; army manuals and everything about the regiment's history. He was capable of anything. I worshipped him and the very ground he slapped his polished hob-nailed boots on.

Jamie had the cot to the right of mine in the dormitory, while the boy on the left was Rodney, also from the same Lancashire town. One moonlit night hands crept out, fingers closed.

'Okay, Rod?'

'No. Come in with me. I'm lonely,' Rodney whispered. Fingers squeezed gently but Jamie was far too close and much too wonderful to lose.

'Come on.'

'Hush. Go to sleep, Rod.'

'I can't. Things are getting on top of me, Jack. I've had enough of this fucking lot. Hold me.'

'Go to sleep.'

'Keep hold. I'll be alright in a minute.'

Holding hands with Rodney, waiting for the nervous lad to fall asleep, wondering if he'll stick it out. Thinking of Duffy, Jamie, all the boys in my life. Will I ever change?

After a few months, Jamie stopped me one day on my way to the mess room. 'Please don't go for dinner,' he said. 'Sit in the barrack room and let's talk.'

'Can't it wait until after dinner?' I asked.

'Please,' he said softly, 'I want to talk in private.'

It was cold. A big coal fire roared up the chimney in our highly polished dormitory room. Jamie sat on a great leather settee, capable of seating ten guys. He seemed a bit nervous, and fidgety. He pulled out a packet of cigarettes and lit two of them in a very intimate way. The very moment I sat beside him we were in each other's arms.

'Hold me close,' he whispered. 'I've had enough! I've had enough, Jackie boy! Hold me for Christ's sake.'

It had been tough but the worst was over. I hugged him and kissed his fair hair. 'Let it go!' I whispered. 'Cry! Get it off your chest. I understand.'

'I'm sorry,' he said. 'I needed someone. Thanks, Jack.'

I kissed him neatly on the forehead. 'It's alright,' I said softly. 'I know how you feel.'

'Do you?' He hugged me and looked me square in the face. 'Do you, Jack? A tough kid from Liverpool? Do you know what they call people like me?'

'Like us, Jamie. People like you and me! I think the bloody world of you.'

'You're the best soldier in the squad,' said the boy. 'Are you trying to tell me you're homosexual? I don't believe it!'

He had to believe it when we kissed like boys in love, and touched stiffened sexual erections. 'Forgive me,' asked Jamie. 'I shouldn't have started all this. I'm sorry.'

I told him I loved him and would die for him.

Seventeen-year-old boys, starved of love and affection, can get very lonely. He said he was lonely and cried on my shoulder.

'Please be serious with me,' I asked. 'I've been through all this before. I couldn't take another beating. I loved a guy so much, I almost died! I was in the army on boy service and when my friend got shipped off to Aden, I couldn't get over it so I pissed off. Don't hurt me, Jamie boy. Love me or leave me, but for Christ's sake make up your mind. I care for you.'

We dried his tear-stained face on his towel and he went off to use the phone at the guard-room. The guys were back from lunch when he returned and sat on my cot.

'I've been in touch with my mother,' he whispered over the din. 'She's going to drive down tomorrow and take us home for the weekend. Will you come, Jackie?'

I squeezed his hand.

'Thanks,' said Jamie.

'I'm not used to posh people with cars and telephones,' I warned him.

'My family aren't posh,' replied the lovely lad. 'They're down-to-earth people. My old man worked damned hard for his telephone and car. You're my best friend, Jackie. Just stop putting fag-ends behind your fucking ear!'

'You mean I ain't got no couth?'

'I hope you're joking,' he said with a smile. Unfortunately, I wasn't.

Saturday morning crept along. Duffy took the lunchtime train and Jamie's mother arrived in an Austin Ten. She was beautiful, fair-haired and fragrant, a laughing voice that tinkled like a bell. Her clothes were just right, neat little hat, perfect dress. The prettiest mother I ever did see.

'So you're Jack? Jamie writes home about you.'

'Oh, uh . . . ' I stammered, blushing scarlet.

Jamie dug me in the ribs. We jumped into the back seat and let his mother drive us from the parade-ground car park in style. Eventually the great black wheels of a mineshaft came into view, a filthy mountain of slag nearby, then lovely country lanes with green, green grass and a late summer harvest. 'Almost home. Wait till you meet the rest of the family.'

Jamie's father worked in a hotel as under-manager, bar manager and receptionist. A busy-looking guy, he wore pin-striped trousers, black morning-coat, polished shoes and silver-grey tie. He greeted me with affection, kissed his wife and son, took the family car and hurried back to work.

Timmy, my friend's younger brother, had only just left school, and worked as an apprentice electrician. Taller than Jamie, he was a fresh-faced youth, fair-haired and handsome. Big square teeth glistened in his firm pink gums. A breathtaking young stripling, he had fine shoulders, laughing blue eyes — a real show-stopper. Another brother worked down the local pit. He was married and lived nearby.

Roast beef and Yorkshire pudding was followed by a stroll through the town, all the kids in steel-shod clogs, skipping rope and talking ee bah gum. A bunch of kids skipped and sang outside the local baker's shop: 'Sikey's bread, 'tis made of lead, if any bugger eats it thee drops down dead!'

'Bugger off!' shouted the baker. The kids kept right on singing and skipping outside Mr Sikey's bread shop.

'I bet he doesn't do much business,' I remarked.

'He used to,' replied Jamie, 'but one of his sons was a blackleg. He refused to join a strike, and now all the people shop at the Co-op. The kids give him a dog's life, and everyone says his cakes are stale.'

I quite believed him. The miners were a very close-knit community.

Most of the streets and roads were named after flowers, and the beautiful things in life that miners loved but seldom saw: Bluebell Avenue, Honeysuckle Road and Jasmine Lane. I thought my friend was joking when he pointed out Lover's Lane from the window of our bus.

'That's where they meet,' he said. 'My brother Tom met his wife down Lover's Lane. Mom and Dad used to go there when they were courting. I bet if you walked down there on a summer's day, you'd find every courting couple in town. Timmy and I used to hide in the grass and watch them.'

'Peeping Toms!' I said with a smile.

'Nothing to peep at,' replied Jamie. 'They only used to kiss and cuddle. If a girl did more than that, the whole town would know about it and she'd get thrown out of home by her dad.'

It was my first ride in a bus and made me feel quite posh. I was used to tramcars and couldn't imagine a community without the old rattlers.

Jamie's room was something special, a treasure house, Aladdin's cave. He'd shared it with his younger brother for years. Books and comics lined the shelves, along with toys and games and footballs, roller skates, a box of snakes and ladders, ludo, draughts and chess, a shrine to their lost childhood. A colourful carpet covered the floor, and there was a double bed against the wall, pretty curtains at the polished window, brightly coloured table lamps and sparkling trophies on the gleaming sideboard — Timmy's presence everywhere. His fragrance filled the room. He'd spent most of his life in this comfortable den, but now he used a room vacated by his married brother. The boy wore pyjamas, and looked a picture when he came to say goodnight.

His brother and I used gym shorts, the sleeping garment of the young soldier. Holding hands came naturally, so I kissed Jamie's cheek and put my hand in his hair. Jamie blushed. 'You don't have to kiss me,' he said.

'I care for you.'

He squeezed my fingers, moved his head aside. I kissed him on the forehead, ran my finger down his cheek. 'Okay, Jamie? some boys kiss. There's nothing wrong with it. We did it at Chester and you didn't seem to mind.'

He put his hands round my neck, pursed his lovely lips, took my kiss and sighed with pleasure. 'Something will happen,' he said quietly. 'Something we'll regret. Kiss me again, Jack.'

I pulled his gym shorts down but he pulled them up again. 'Stop it!'

'What's wrong, Jamie? I care for you. We've done it before!'

'Leave my pants alone. You'll go too far. Just hold me. I thought you liked to kiss.'

'I want to . . . I want to . . . I want you, Jamie. I want to kiss every part of you, and do it properly, make love to you.'

He closed his eyes, all shy and fluttery, hugged me tight beneath the arms. I pulled my pants off and felt his hands around my neck.

'Don't take my knickers down,' said the boy. 'Please don't.'

I kissed his hairs and he held my erection, shy young eyelids partly closed. Sexy and stiff, we hugged each other. He took me in his hand, put me beneath him and felt the stiffness between his legs.

'Okay?'

'Yes. I'm alright now.'

'You're lovely!' I replied. 'Let me do it properly.'

I kissed him, held his lovely thing and tasted the slippery tip.

'You've been with other boys,' said Jamie.

'And so have you. Let me kiss your bottom.'

'Don't go too far,' he said shyly. 'Just a kiss.'

His bottom now slippery and wet with love, his long legs stretched across the bed.

'Don't do that! Don't! Please don't!'

'Please, Jamie.' Slippery fluid ran from me, trickled on the soft warm skin, ran across the most exciting spot.

Jamie held himself apart, hands flat on his bottom, the magic moment almost there. 'Do it!' he said excitedly. 'Fuck me if you want to.'

Slippy and shiny and scarlet with love, the tip vanished. Jamie put his hands on the pillow and raised his bottom. It sank deep. Jamie sighed with pleasure, gripped the edge of the bed, came back for more.

'There! It's done! Alright?'

'Yes. Don't stop! Make love to me!'

'I want to see your face, Jamie.'

'No. Don't take it out. Please. Not yet.'

I moved away, kissed his bottom and pulled him to the edge of the mattress.

'It's better like this, Jamie.'

'I'm not a girl.'

'You're beautiful.'

He saw my penis vanish, felt the thrusting love and spilt his semen on his belly. He clung on tight, perspiration at his brow, tears in his bright blue eyes.

'Happy?'

'Are you?'

'Mmmm! You're lovely. Sorry I hurt you.'

'It's alright, Jack. I wanted it. Wanted it for a long time. Just never went that far before. You know I love you.'

'I love you too. I know how you feel, kid. My schoolfriend made love to me and I couldn't do without him.'

'And me. My schoolfriend was like you, but I wouldn't let him do it properly.'

He cried and I stroked the tears away. 'We'll get used to each other, kid. Don't cry.

Weekends came and weekends went, but they were never the same as that first time, the magic had gone. Jamie always slept with his firm litle bottom pressed into me, but each time a move was made he rejected it, so I turned from him and let him come to me. It always brought us together, but Jamie was content with a form of kissing love. It was very beautiful and ended with an ejaculation that sent us to sleep in each other's arms. Yet it wasn't quite what I needed, even though the kisses landed in the most intimate spots and satisfied us both.

It was one of those grand and glorious days, a day of wonder and excitement, twenty-four hours that only come once in a boy's life. The training was done, finished, over. We could all go back home if we wanted.

The band and drums came out to play. Sweet music filled the Castle grounds and the sergeant-major ponced about in all his pomp and polished glory.

'Who's signing on for seven years?'

'I am!' said Rodney. 'I'm not going down the mines like my old man. I'm gonna be a soldier.'

'And me!'

'And me!'

'Me too!'

'I'm with you,' said Duffy.

All in together, all my mates, my sweetheart and sweet Rodney. What a wonderful day!

It was late 1938 and talk of war was on everybody's lips and in the daily press. It hadn't changed anything in military establishments. Training went on as before, though not for August squad. We were given three weeks' leave and a railway warrant for Aldershot, the home of the British army, where the second battalion lived in Maida Barracks.

I planned to spend some of my leave with Duffy in Liverpool and the rest of the holiday at Jamie's home. Rodney hadn't come into my reckoning. We were girl friends, shared each other's sexy secrets and discussed the boys we loved. He was a very gentle young creature, sensitive, kind and caring, a real teenage boy on the surface, but somewhere in his fine young soldier's make-up lay the real Rodney, a sweet feminine lad who wanted a man.

The world of the homosexual boy was ours and we talked about it openly. 'Three weeks is a long time to be apart,' he said. 'We'll miss each other, Jack. Stay at my home for a few days or call and see me. I live near Jamie.'

It seemed like a good idea, so I accepted his kind invitation and promised to call on him after my stay in Liverpool.

Liverpool hadn't changed much — queues outside the picture houses, untidy lads at every street corner, nowhere to go, nothing to do. Sex, however, came knocking at my door.

Duffy was a proud young soldier. He liked to take a drink in a pub, show off his smart uniform and treat his friends to a beer. I went along with him, enjoyed his company and ushered him into the saloon of an old neighbourhood public house. Johnny Fitz, the publican's son, worked behind the bar. He'd always been in my heart and still came to me in erotic dreams and hand-held fantasies — the first lover, the big boy who'd taken my twelve-year-old virginity. I could never forget it. It seemed that Johnny hadn't forgotten either.

I liked Johnny. He was twenty-two now, much too old for me but very attractive. He welcomed us and asked me to stay when the pub closed. There was nothing else to do, so I walked with Duffy to the tram stop, said goodnight and returned to the boozer and Johnny Fitz.

Johnny shared a room with his young brother, a schoolboy of fourteen. They used separate beds and I was invited into Johnny's warm nest. While Johnny was still in the bathroom, Gerry and I were in the bedroom. He kicked off his shoes and I peeled off my shirt.

'Do you know Flash Barker?' he asked.

I climbed out of my trousers. 'You mean Flash Gordon?'

Gerry removed his shirt. 'No,' he said. 'I mean Flash Barker. He's a Yank, an American wrestler. Come to the stadium with me and Johnny tomorrow and you'll see him.'

We'd known each other since early childhood, slept sometimes in the same bed and shared the same cup, but Gerry was four years my junior and I thought we had nothing in common. Then he pulled his trousers down and I admired his naked beauty. A black-headed Irish boy, a perfect specimen of youth, he looked magnificent. His sexual parts were sheer perfection, complete and fully loaded. A long penis, thin and very white-skinned and pointed, hung from a cliff of testicles and looked exceptionally beautiful against a background of new pubic hair, shiny black and neat as paint on his belly.

Gerry picked up a gym vest. 'This is my nightie,' he said. He pulled the vest on, a colourful little slip with a number on the back. It certainly looked attractive, but didn't quite cover his bottom.

'I wear shorts.'

'I don't,' replied the boy. His long white dickie looked enticing, semi-erect and getting longer by the second.

A door slammed shut on the landing. Gerry took a flying leap through the air. 'Here's Johnny!' he said as he landed on his bed.

Johnny wasted no time. He knew what he wanted and went for it immediately. But the magic had gone — it just didn't work for me, even if the original scene would still play its never-ending part in my fantasies. For my handsome lover, however, the second honeymoon seemed to work out well. He relived the seduction of his twelve-year-old boy, whispered some words of love and kissed me tenderly before he fell asleep.

I liked him still, but couldn't stop thinking of his sleeping brother in the next bed. I loved young boys! Especially beautiful, beautiful boys like Gerry Fitz.

It was Gerry who woke me up the next morning, put a cup of coffee in my hand and sat on the bed while I drank it.

'Where's Johnny?' I asked.

'In the bar, sleepyhead. It's ten o'clock. Get out of bed. We've got to go to the stadium and join the sports club.'

The boy smiled when I pulled my knickers on.

'I thought you slept in shorts,' he said wickedly.

'What's wrong with sleeping in the nude?'

'You ought to know,' said the smiling boy. 'Come on. Let's get going.'

All-in wrestling wasn't publicly allowed in Liverpool. However, you could join the Liverpool Stadium Sports Club, sign the membership book and purchase a ticket for a private exhibition of wrestling for members only. These bouts took place on Sunday afternoons, when thousands of sports fans packed the great hall. Tickets were reasonably cheap, even with the one shilling membership fee. The brothers were members but I wasn't, so Gerry and I joined a queue that seemed to stretch for a mile.

Gerry bought a sixpenny programme at the gate. 'Wow!' he chortled, lovely face all pink and glowing with excitement. 'Look at today's bill: "Flash Barker, USA. Jack Pye, Doncaster. Harry Pye, Doncaster. The Anaconda from Africa. Man Mountain Dean. The Green Asp — a Mystery Man in a mask!!! Who is the Mystery Man of Europe?"

'It's gonna be smashing!' Gerry shouted. 'Ted Baxter's the referee. Wait till you see Ted! He always wears a green shirt and somebody always rips it off and tears it to bits. Wait till you see this lot . . .'

The excitement was infectious. I'd never seen a wrestling match, nor even heard of all-in wrestling. It was all new to me. Luckily enough, we managed to get three good seats, not exactly ringside but as near as possible. Gerry insisted on paying, though it was Johnny's treat really. He'd supplied the cash and could well afford it. Chattering away like excited schoolkids, we grabbed a tram and returned to the pub for Sunday dinner.

The stadium was packed, with ringsiders in evening dress, black bow-ties and snow-white shirts. Cigar smoke filled the air with the fragrance of Havana, while Burmese cheroots glowed and stank abominably. Barefoot kids ran through the aisles selling programmes at the top of their voices. A dense crowd of Liverpudlians, flat-capped, white-mufflered and jabbering happily, filled the cheapest sections — standing room only, the peasants' gallery, exactly like a football gathering. These everyday Joes were separated from the posh seats of the wealthy by the medium-priced seats, packed with men and boys to form a human barrier.

Brilliant lights gleamed over the ring, a colourful centrepiece of red and white rope, canvas, timber and padded steel stanchions: the square arena, the loneliest place in the world.

'Laydeez an' gennelmen . . . ' bawled the referee.

'It's Ted Baxter!' shouted young Gerry. 'Look! He's gorreez green shirt on!'

' . . . introdoocin' . . .'

'TearIz shirt off!' shouted a loud scouse voice from the shilling stands. 'Teariz friggin' shirt off!'

Gerry grabbed me by the arm. 'That guy comes here every week,' he said. 'I wonder who he is.'

Ted Baxter finished his spiel, and all the lights went out.

'Put the fucken' lights on!' shouted the voice.

'Lissen him!' said the excited boy at my side. 'He's gorra voice like a foghorn.'

The lights shone over the bright arena once again, the crowd settled down and two muscle-bound grapplers came down the aisle. The preliminary bout was reasonable enough: a catchweight opener, a skilful exhibition by two great athletes, but not worth screaming your head off for. A slow handclap greeted the second pair of contestants.

'It's Jack Pye and the Man Mountain,' explained my enthusiastic friend.

'What's the slow handclap for?'

'Because they're dirty fighters and nobody likes them.'

Jack Pye climbed into the ring, grabbed the referee and tore the shirt from his back. The crowd screamed: 'Ripirrup! Ripirrup! Tear the fucken' thing to bits!'

Man Mountain Dean thumped his chest, grabbed Jack Pye by the throat and smashed him in the face.

'Oooo! Oooo! Oooo! Dirty bastard. Oooo! Oooo! Oooo!' screamed the stomping crowd.

Baxter's shirt went sailing out of the ring. Ted shot between the ropes, hung by his toes and rescued the bright green shirt at the very last moment. Meanwhile Jack Pye took advantage of his absence to smash a stool on the Man Mountain.

'Dirty Pye! Dirty Pye! Oooo! Oooo! Dirty Pye!'

Man Mountain appealed to the referee and Ted went into a pantomime act. He pointed to his eye, then to the ringside and finally to his lovely shirt. Man Mountain grabbed it, waved it round his head and shot around the ring like a two-year-old with Ted running after him. The Mountain stopped dead, the referee crashed into him and collapsed in a heap with his arms outstretched.

'One! Two! Three!' chanted the crowd.

Jack Pye came flying through the air, landing feet first on Man Mountain's chest only to crash out cold by the referee.

'Four! Five!' chanted the crowd.

The guy with the foghorn voice got them going again: 'Teariz friggen' shirt!'

Man Mountain lost his temper and stomped from the ring with the shirt held high. The crowd screamed abuse and finished with a slow handclap.

'Laydeez an' gennlemen! Please! Order please! Let's have a little attention,' called the referee, speaking into a microphone: 'Final decision! No contest!'

'Get your friggen' shirt on!'

'Flash Barker's on next,' Gerry said. 'He's my hero.'

Flash was something from another world — scarlet-lined cloak of gold, scarlet tassels and gilded boots, golden skin and hair and a beautiful smile on his handsome face. He minced into the ring like a fairy.

'Gerrem down!' called the voice in the crowd. 'Gerrem down an' give us a flash!'

Flash took a bow, removed his cloak and went through the first steps in ballet, one hand on the topmost rope and the other on his gold-covered hip.

'Seconds out!' said a voice over the mike. 'Time!'

The man in the mask looked scary but he didn't scare Flash. 'The Green Asp has never been beaten,' said Gerry. 'Neither has Flash Barker. This'll be a great fight!'

Full Nelsons, Irish whips, Boston crabs and the Indian death lock. But Flash spent most of his time trying to remove the mystery man's mask.

'Leave the bleedin' thing alone!' shouted the foghorn voice. 'What's up, wack? Do you wanna kissim?'

Flash went into a two-fisted stance, smashed the guy in the mask into unconsciousness and got himself disqualified. The crowd roared, a new bout commenced and Ted Baxter wore his bright green shirt again. This time the Anaconda got a warning for foul play, so he tore Baxter's shirt from his back and ripped it into a thousand pieces. The crowd went mad.

'Did you like it?' Gerry said outside.

'Never had such a good time in all me life!'

The pubs opened at 7 p.m., so Johnny went on duty and worked behind the bar with his mother. Gerry and I cleared the family table, washed the dishes and settled down in the living room.

Duffy expected me to spend the evening propping up the bar and talking to his old man. It wasn't my idea of a good time, so I just let things ride and hoped my mate would understand. Wrestling on the carpet with young Gerry Fitz was much more interesting and became quite exciting. He knew all the holds and grips. Nose to nose, Gerry on top, freckled cheek at my lips, erections hard and digging into bellies.

'I hope you're staying tonight,' he said.

'Yes, and I'm not sleeping with your brother.'

He burst out laughing and I rolled on top.

'Are you going to wear your shorts?' he said, taking me in a scissor hold, long lean legs around my waist, gripping hard and squeezing. I took his hair, pulled him close and kissed him on the lips.

Gerry struggled free and ran into the kitchen. 'That's enough!' he giggled. 'Let's have a cup of tea.'

The family returned at half past ten and found us playing cards.

When the game lost its interest, Gerry got the draught board out, set up the counters, placed a black in one hand, a white in the other and put them behind his back.

'Don't be there all night,' said his mother. 'We're going to bed.'

'And me,' said Johnny. 'See you upstairs.'

I chose white and Gerry made the first move.,

'What are we playing for?' he asked. 'A penny a game?'

'You know what we're playing for.'

'Okay,' said the boy. 'So do you.'

He lost a couple of men, I lost a couple of men and Gerry got a crown.

'What are we playing for?' he enquired. 'My bed?'

'Mmmm!'

'You'd better win then. It should be fun sleeping with you.'

The house was silent when we climbed the stairs and made our way to the shared bedroom. Johnny was already sleeping soundly as Gerry removed his clothes and slipped the running vest over his fine young body. My arm went round his waist and he came to me, all silky skin and soft lips.

'Are we going to play?' he asked quietly.

'Mmmm! All night long. Any game you like.'

The streets were damp when I hit the road and went in search of Duffy, the only friend I had who wasn't of my own kind. Some mysterious chemistry kept us together but I felt a little guilty about the relationship and knew it wasn't quite right.

I should have told him, explained things, but he wouldn't have understood. How could he? The whole subject was distasteful. Simple jokes were passed from time to time and the word pansy was in use. What was a pansy? I certainly wasn't and neither were my friends. I had to be with my own kind, my own gender, ordinary guys who didn't wear a label but knew exactly what they were. We knew each other by mating instinct and natural body movements.

Duffy was so very close and yet so far away. He was waiting for me, Big Duffy, all smiles and soft fair hair.

'Let's get our photographs taken,' he said, 'both of us on the same print. Okay?'

He puzzled me at times, but I knew in my heart it was pure friendship and felt the embrace of his brotherly love. At Jerome's on the London Road you could get three colour prints for a shilling.

'Hey mister,' called a kid with a fish in a jar. 'Are you gonna get your picture taken?'

'Bugger off!' said Duffy.

'You'll crack the fucken' camera!' said the kid's pal. 'If I had a face like yours, I'd pawn it an' lose the bleedin' ticket.'

'Fucken' kids!' said my mate. 'Were you ever like that?'

'All the time.'

'And me. What a fucken' town! Roll on Aldershot!'

He stuck a cigarette in his mouth and led the way into the studio.

'Perfectly still!' said the young photographer. A handsome pair, cigarettes in smiling lips. 'Not a move! Smile please. There we are! I'll have them hand-tinted for you. Call back in half an hour.'

'Let's play snooker,' said Duffy.

'I don't like snooker,' I replied, trying to give him a clue and make him understand. 'I don't like pubs and I can't stand football matches.'

'You play football every day,' he said.

'That's not what I mean.'

'What the hell do you mean?'

'I'm different, I guess. Don't do what the other guys do.'

'Bollocks!' Oblivious to it all, Duffy took me into a London Road pub. 'Gentlemen only,' read the notice on the billiard-room door. 'Collar and tie must be worn.' Duffy set the balls up and it took half an hour to knock them down again. Great stuff!

Pictures, pubs and snooker — it went on for a couple of days until I caught the train to Wigan, the clickety-clack of wheel and rail in my ears and Duffy on my mind. I wasn't too sophisticated but the simple things in life were not for me. I had to have a mate, a masculine one of my own, someone who could satisfy my hunger. It wasn't Duffy and it certainly wasn't Rodney, though I called on him because he cared.

'Well!' said Mrs Dunlop when she saw me. 'Come in, lad. Jamie's not home. He's in Lancaster with his cousin. Have you had your supper?'

'Yes, thank you,' I replied. 'I've been eating all day long.'

'Well, you can have a cup of cocoa, can't you?'

'Lovely,' I said. 'Thanks.'

'Did you enjoy yourself in Liverpool?' she asked in the kitchen.

'Nothing special,' I answered. 'I went to the movies with my friend, and we had our photographs taken.'

'My!' she said when she saw the pictures. 'Who's the big lad? Duffy?'

'Yes.'

'It's a lovely picture. 'You and Jamie will have to get one like that. Oh I'm so glad you're all going together. Have you seen Rodney yet?'

'Mmmm!' I murmured. 'Only left their house ten minutes ago.'

'He's a handsome lad,' she said sweetly, 'but I never thought he'd make a soldier. He was always so timid and nervous.'

Timmy came in from the living-room, big smile and shiny teeth.

'There you are!' said his mother. 'Be a good lad and make the cocoa. I've so many things to do.'

The boy reached out, took the photographs from my hand and moved beneath the kitchen light. 'She's gone to make our bed,' he said, gazing intently at the hand-tinted prints. 'You're bunking in with me tonight, okay?'

'Suits me.'

'Can I have one of these?'

'Take one,' I replied.

He fished a leather wallet from an inside pocket and stuffed the photograph inside. 'Thanks,' he said. 'I'm having an Eccles cake with my cocoa. Would you like a couple?'

The Eccles cakes were big and flat and round and flaky, stuffed with currants and glossy with sugar. A delicious smell filled the kitchen, spicy currants and demerara. Timmy emptied his cup, took the photograph from his wallet and looked at it for the umpteenth time. 'I like the cigarette in the mouth,' he said. 'Real Humphrey Bogart stuff!'

Humphrey Bogart wasn't sleeping with him.

There was a fragrance about the boy, a special kind of smell; his mother's crispy sheets, fluffy towels and fresh pyjamas, a lovely scent that filled the warm bed we shared. The attractive youngster hardly stirred, flat on his back, hands at his side, damp fair hair on the pillow. 'Alright?' he asked as I twisted and turned.

'Just restless,' I said. 'It's the strange bed I suppose.'

He slipped an arm beneath my neck. 'Settle down,' he said. 'Get comfortable.'

It wasn't as easy as that. The brotherly embrace, innocent hold and magic touch of the boy's skin made me shake. He pulled me close. 'Still restless?' he said, hugging me in, hand on my shoulder.

'Not used to you, I guess.'

His grip tightened and my cheek fell naturally to his chest. Sexually aroused, Timmy pulled his jacket open and lay back comfortably with my hand in his pants. 'You're just like my brother,' he said gently. 'Play with it if you want.'

His face came close, lips touched lips and his tongue went in my mouth. I sucked it hard and gripped his lovely cock. It was big, a perfect tool of love, long and thick and very hard, a wondrous thing of beauty. He rolled on his back, took me along and squeezed me belly to bare belly. 'I'm going to cock you, pretty boy.'

I took his face in my hands, kissed his lips and told him he was very handsome.

A hard mound of stiffened tissue grew from him, sinewy, steel-strong and exciting. I stroked it with my fingertips; two, three, six inches passed beneath my touch before I reached the soft round balls of flesh, travelled the horny length, felt its pulse, its hardened tip and the heat in my palm.

Bellies tight, he squeezed me hard, gripped my waist and put his lips in my hair. He crouched like a young lion, knees apart, the astonishing thing beneath him, testicles hanging — a stallion! He looked magnificent, a polished statue, shapely and demanding. I kissed the incredible tool, crawled beneath and waited. He mated with an exciting stab, a real hard thrust of love that made me squeal. Bone hard, he drove right in, forceful, experienced.

'Quiet!'

He forced me apart with his hands, sent the loving instrument home and made me squeal again. 'Oh Timmy!'

'Shh! Keep still.'

I sucked in my breath. 'Oh Timmy.'

His hairs touched my bottom and I reached beneath and felt the sinewy mound. A boy inside me, all the way, every beautiful inch. That's what I was meant for. A loving boy to thrill me, fill me with his magic seed and whisper words of love. Timmy cared. He held me close and kissed me tenderly.

'You should have been a girl,' he said affectionately.

'I feel like a girl sometimes. Hold me tight.'

'Relax,' he whispered. 'Jamie will be here tomorrow. He'll make love to you every night.'

'Jamie's not like that.'

He put me beneath him, felt the warm semen flow, kissed me when I sighed with pleasure.

'Tell me about my brother,' he said. 'I'd love to know.'

'Nothing to tell,' I replied. 'Really.'

'There must be. You sleep together, Jack. He must fuck you.'

'Jamie doesn't touch me. We're just friends.'

He dug his great erection in my belly. 'You're so big!' I said . . .

A watery winter sun awakened me, shone through the polished window and brought me to my senses. Timmy had gone, his pyjamas folded neatly on the pillow.

Fluffy towel about my waist, I left the room and bumped into the boy's mother on the landing.

'You're putting on weight,' she said in her lilting Lancashire voice, poking a finger into my breast. 'Did you sleep alright?'

'Marvellous! I'm still dreaming.'

A strange emotion drew me to his toothbrush so I used it, and the physical sense of pleasure made my penis rise. I washed and used his towel to dry my bottom.

3. Garrison Town

Aldershot was two separate communiuties. There was a population of everyday people who lived in little boxes, curtains at the
polished windows, gardens front and rear, bicycles at the
pavement's edge, washing on the line and well-dressed schoolkids
playing cricket in the tidy streets and lanes.

Then there was the imposing garrison town, a huge sprawling
metropolis of barrack blocks, gymnasiums, weapon training
schools, gleaming parade grounds, all whitewash trim and
fluttering flags. Great colourful badges from every regiment in the
British army were displayed by the spotless roads and tree-lined
avenues.

My neighbours were a thousand guys from the Grenadier
Guards. The house across the road contained four companies of
Yorkshire Light Infantry, and just behind the green lawns of my
commanding officer lived hundreds of beautiful boys in tartan
skirts. Uniformed youths strolled the well-kept sidewalks. Armour-
plated trucks, bren-gun carriers and heavy-duty tanks rolled past
the window with not a civilian in sight.

This was the home of the British army, its nerve centre, a
gun-bristling nucleus set in the rolling countryside of Hampshire,
surrounded by gorse-blue grass and bluebell-covered woods.
Young athletes trained on the open sports fields, threw the javelin,
tossed the hammer, spun the discus and romped around in floppy
training suits, open necked and ankle tight.

We belonged to a heavy machine-gun regiment. Jamie and I
were in 'C' company, he as the company commander's clerk, and I
as a lance-corporal. It was the obvious post for young Jamie but I
was very much surprised to find myself promoted during my first
few days in the battalion.

'You're the youngest NCO in the regiment,' said the RSM.
There's a lot of old soldiers here and they'll treat you with scorn if
you let 'em. It's up to you, son! Be a bastard! Put the insubordinate
buggers on a charge and I'll see that they're punished. They'll
respect you when they find that you'll stand for no nonsense, and

they'll do what you tell 'em. A good NCO has to be a downright bastard. Do you want further promotion?'

'Yes sir!' I replied smartly.

'Go out and be a bastard!' said the RSM. 'Dis...miss!'

It wasn't as easy as all that. NCOs were not allowed to mix with private soldiers and Jamie couldn't even have a cup of tea in the canteen with me. I had to use the corporals' mess, a separate canteen. Fortunately, all the guys mixed at the garrison cinema, a special movie house for troops only.

'It's not worth it,' I said to my friend in the cinema. 'I'm throwing in my stripe, kid.'

'Don't be stupid!' he replied. 'I'll catch up with you in a few months. Christ, Jack! What's wrong with you? We need promotion. We need the extra pay that goes with it. Have a bit of fucking sense!'

Complications set in when Jamie slipped away to London on a weekend pass. I waited up all night, sat on his bed and fell asleep fully dressed. He avoided me for a few weeks, spent all his time in the office and practically ran 'C' company single-handed.

The old soldiers that the RSM had warned me about had served time in India, Palestine and all parts of the British Empire. Naturally, they objected to an eighteen-year-old boy giving orders and instructions on the Vickers machine-gun; they were experts and had been in action with the very same weapon.

Some of the guys were reasonably young, lazy and needed instruction, and I had to get on with the lessons. I could be a downright bastard and throw my weight about, but it meant a lot of hassle and I would have no friends at all. On the other hand, I could be an easy-going, cushy NCO and be despised for inefficiency. The choice was mine.

I tried a sensible approach and stuck to my guns, demanding attention when I spoke during M.G. instruction because I loved the weapon and was quite expert with it.

'Cut the bullshit!' said a guy named Andy Lee. 'Let's have a smoke. You're only a red-arsed recruit! If I had you in India, you'd be my buddly-buddly boy.'

The term 'buddly-buddly' was Hindi for 'change about'; roughly translated in the language of the soldier, it meant: You do me, I do you.

The section looked on to see my reaction, which was pure dockland Scouse! 'Shut your fucken' hole, Private Lee,' I said quietly and menacingly. 'I could break your fucken' ugly nose and you wouldn't know what hit you. You pox-ridden bastid!'

I thought of insulting him further, luring him into the boxing ring and giving him a hiding in front of his mates. However, it would not have brought respect. Respect is something you earn without resorting to violence and I knew that.

The battalion was childish and dull. The men acted like girls at a private boarding school, telling silly tales and spreading gossip. It was not what I expected from the army. I was still a good soldier, and dreamed my childish dream of fighting some glorious battle.

There was a battalion athletic team, however, so I joined and lost myself in the gym: training, boxing, running and all kinds of sport. Jamie and I drifted apart. I could hardly sleep for thinking about him, and lay awake at night wondering where, and with whom, he spent his weekends.

As I grew to understand the simple working life of the battalion, so I progressed, made a few athletic friends and discovered that the guys in the athletic team could get away with absolutely anything as long as they were in training. Life was full, but I became lonely and cast my net in other directions.

A canteen is a liquor vessel carried by soldiers. There is another kind of canteen — a sutling house. A sutling house is run by a sutler, a person who follows the army as a seller of refreshments.

Many years ago, a fine young man name Smith teamed up with another colleague and together they created an institute that catered for the young soldier who did not want to get drunk, fondle the filthy barrack-rats and pay his miserable wages to the whores provided by the sutler.

The Smith-D'reen was an institute not unlike the YMCA and there was one near Maida Barracks, Aldershot. It was a very quiet establishment. Young soldiers, lonely and far away from home, gathered there. They were gentle souls and liked to relax in the comfortable armchairs, read from a fine selection of books, modern paperbacks and the daily newspapers. They could sit in comfort, write to their loved ones and use the modern showers and bathrooms provided for them.

The guy in charge of the private bath-house and individual bathrooms was a quiet young man named Taffy. He had a strange reputation and was known by most of the boys in Aldershot as a 'cocksucker'.

Rodney sat in the lounge of the Smith-D'reen, a book in his hand and a towel round his neck. 'Hi Rod,' I said in a friendly voice. Where's your pal?'

His boyfriend was a nice kid named Kelly, and they were never apart. I thought perhaps they were in love but it wasn't obvious, not even to a guy like me.

'We fell out,' he said simply. He looked a bit low. I liked him and had always been attracted by his pleasant boy's face and shock of stiff straight hair, which stood up like a well-trimmed hedge. There was nothing outwardly feminine or beautiful about young Rod. He was a boy, pure and simple; a gorgeous natural boy — slim, athletic and bursting with life and energy. He smelled like a boy — chewing-gum and chocolate biscuits, Kit-Kat bars and toffee.

'Looks like you came for a bath,' said Rodney when he saw my towel.

Taffy came mincing into the lounge with his hand on his hip. 'Whoo!' he said before I could open my mouth. 'I didn't know there were two of you. I'll go and run another bath.'

Rodney's face broke out in a big broad smile. 'I'm sure it's just an act,' he said to me. 'Nobody would piss about like that unless they were joking. Do you think he's funny?'

'What do you mean by funny?' I asked.

'Comical,' replied Rod. I think he should be on the fuckin' stage. He makes me piss myself.'

Taffy came back a few minutes later, put one hand behind his neck, pushed at his extra long hair with his palm and said with a friendly smile on his face, 'Your baths are ready. If there's anything else you need, just ring the bell.'

'Like what?' Rodney asked.

'Ooo, soap maybe...shampoo? How the hell do I know?' remarked Taffy.

'We've got everything,' replied the boy, producing a twopenny tablet of Lifebuoy soap.

'I bet you have,' answered the bath attendant. 'This way, boys. I've put you together. Don't worry, there's a bolt on the door.'

'Cheeky bugger,' remarked Rodney in a theatrical aside. 'He's a real fuckin' comic singer.'

When Taffy said he had put us together, he meant we'd be sharing a room with two tubs. Rodney and I had used the communal showers, tubs and changing-rooms in the barrack blocks a thousand times. We had walked naked among our comrades and thought nothing of stripping off in front of anyone.

Taffy stood in the bathroom and enjoyed himself as we hung up our clothes. 'I'll stay and wash your hair if you like,' he remarked hopefully. 'You boys should come here more often.'

'Bugger off!' said Rodney. He was smiling and a pink blush crept over his boyish cheek as he bolted the door. 'Fuckin' comic singer,' he repeated and jumped into his tub.

Soapy lather ran from my hair, down the valley between my chest muscles and floated on the bluish-white water as I sang softly, without a care in the world. The freedom of the private bathroom comforted me.

'I suppose you get lonely without Jamie Dunlop,' Rodney said across the steamy room. 'You must miss him.'

The unexpected words hit me like a dart from Cupid's arrow and made my sex rise. 'Dreadfully!' I replied. 'I'm lost without him.'

Suddenly I felt a kinship with the boy, and knew he was seeking comfort. 'I don't know why the hell you fell out with Kelly,' I said, 'and it's none of my business, but if I were you I'd try and patch it up. You were as close as two peas in a pod.'

'Just like you and Jamie,' answered the lad, laughing nervously and rubbing at his spiky hair.

'Exactly!' was all I said, and stood up hard and horny in my tub. The white soapy stream ran into my pubic curls, and the stiffened organ shone pink and white beneath a soapy gloss.

Rodney stood up too. 'I'm lonely as hell!' he said. 'Do you want to jump in here with me?'

We clung together in the warm water. 'Jesus! I love a boy like you,' I whispered softly.

'I know! I know!' said lovely Rod. 'I've always known.'

'Hold me Rod,' I replied. 'Jesus Christ! Just hold me.' He was the only one who really understood. Sex raised its lovely shiny heads and we made love like boys. We kissed because it came naturally and the love-making that followed was a great comfort, but we were not in love and it didn't happen again. However, I knew that if I needed a shoulder to cry on, young Rodney would be there, and he would listen.

The next time I saw him, he was queueing outside the garrison cinema with his friend Kelly. I waved and shouted, 'Hi Rod! Everything okay?'

'Just great, Lance Jack!' he shouted above the many heads. The incident made me happy, but didn't cure my loneliness.

The peacetime army thrived on gossip. Guys spoke about brilliant NCOs who'd been busted for having a love affair with a comrade, and a couple of years later regained their stripes because they were such magnificent soldiers. I could hardly believe that such things happened but they did. It seemed the army accepted such affairs in places like India and other parts of the British Empire.

All the ex-Indian soldiers spoke of having a 'buddly-buddly' chum at some time or another during their service. I quite believed them and thought most professional soldiers were possibly homosexual, definitely bisexual, and accepted love among comrades if only in certain circumstances. Common sense told me I was wrong, and yet it was all around me and could be seen by everyone.

I had chosen to live in a world without women and so had my fellow soldiers. The more I thought about these things, the clearer they became. Even the toughest sportsmen and athletes in the regiment had a close male friend and, apart form the few guys who lived in married quarters with their wives and families, were seldom known to associate with girls. Sex has to have an outlet. Perhaps the guys will change as they mature, I thought. Perhaps it is a natural phase in a young man's life. However, I liked being homosexual and knew I would never change.

Unfortunately, the only people who really interested me were very, very beautiful boys. Not the feminine cute young things that one saw from time to time in the pool or gym, winking and acting coy, but real natural boys with boyish beauty in their eyes.

One such creature was Jackie Clithero and he was the most wonderful looking boy I had ever laid eyes on. Jackie was a bugler. I took to following him about; waiting for him to go on guard duty and listening to his beautiful music. Sometimes I waited in the shadows, watched him march to his post and sound off.

'Christ!' said a dreamy-eyed private in 'C' company. 'I could listen to Clithero forever. What a musician!'

There was no chance of making contact; the kids in the band were locked away at night like nuns in a convent. However, he was the only one for me. Jamie had moved to the officers' quarters where he worked as a servant. I thought I'd lost him forever and began to think of Jackie Clithero.

It was a fine spring day when I breasted the tape in a hurdles race and won a bronze medal. A kid came running from the crowd, tears streaming down his face. 'Jesus! What a race!' he exclaimed. 'What's your name?'

'Just call me Lance Jack,' I replied. 'That's the lowest form of animal life in the friggin' British army.'

Exciting sporting events affect young enthusiasts in this way and it was quite common for a lad to shed tears of joy at a well-attended meeting. When I hit the showers and realised the lad was Jackie Clithero, it made me more determined than ever to meet the gorgeous creature.

The following Sunday I found myself kneeling beside him in church. 'Hiya, Lance Jack!' whispered the beautiful boy. Our long slim legs touched as we knelt together. He smelled of healthy boy, that wonderful smell of youthful fragrance I adored in a lad. He was so fresh and delightful — handsome boyish face, and bright blue eyes aglow with mischief.

I'd like to get to know you,' I whispered softly.

We shared a hymn book, and Jackie's long cool fingers touched mine as we turned the pages nervously.

'I'll meet you on the Farnham Road,' said Clithero. 'You ain't the only sportsman in the fuckin' battalion. I run for HQ company. Go for a run after lunch and you'll find me waiting for you.' I liked him even more because he swore in church.

When you are lonely and meet a boy like Jackie Clithero, your heart sings and you forget about everything else. Jamie was never out of my heart for a second, but Jackie was sitting on a five-barred gate on the Farnham Road waiting for me.

'Hiya, Lance Jack!' he said with a cheeky grin. He wore a red and white tracksuit. His jet black hair glistened in the afternoon sun and his white teeth gleamed in his lovely fresh mouth. 'This way!' he shouted, and jumped onto a bridle-path leading across open country. There was a recognised run that the athletes used. A few guys could be seen in the distance when we sat down, but we were well away from the beaten track, almost hidden by long green grass and wild spring flowers.

'So what's it all about?' asked the handsome lad.

'I just want to get to know you,' I replied. 'I thought we could be friends.'

'Oh yeah!' said Clithero. 'Like holding hands in church?'

I wasn't sure about him and thought he might be making fun of me.

'I'm sorry,' I said. 'I'll piss off if it bothers you.'

'You ain't bothering me,' said the lad. 'Don't be so fuckin' touchy. I've been in the army for four fuckin' years. I came right out of an orphanage. Lots of guys have tried to get me in their bed. That's what it's all about, isn't it?'

'Not really,' I replied. 'I only want to be friends. I like you. I joined up with my pal from Chester. This fuckin' stripe came between us and now he's pissed off and I'm lonely.'

Jackie stretched his long lean frame on the grass and chewed on a stalk. 'Do I know him?' asked the fascinating boy.

'You might,' I answered. 'Jamie Dunlop. He was the company clerk but now he's an officer's servant and I never set eyes on the bugger.'

'And you want me to take his place?' asked the gorgeous young bugler.

'I'm sorry,' I replied. 'I know you're only a kid but I would like to make friends just the same.'

'You're only a fuckin' kid yourself!' said the lad. 'A stripe on your arm don't make you a fuckin' man! I'm the same age as you! My boy service ends this month.' He seemed aggressive, so I got to my feet and brushed the loose grass from my tracksuit.

'Don't go,' said Jackie Clithero. 'I'd like to make friends with you.'

We sat quite close. 'You can find a nice boy every night of the week,' he said. 'Why pick on me? The garrison cinema is crawling with nice lads looking for a friend.'

'Maybe so,' I replied. 'I don't go chasing other guys. I only want you. I don't really make many friends but when I do I want to stay with them for ever. I can't quite believe my last friend let me down. I'm very much alone and this bloody stripe makes it worse.'

'I've been lonely too,' he admitted. 'I don't piss about with guys but I know I'm like you and Jamie Dunlop. You recognised it. That's why you followed me about, isn't it?'

'Yes,' I said softly. 'I could see it in your eyes.'

'I'm afraid to go out with anyone,' said the boy. 'This place is like a fuckin' old ladies' home. Christ knows what would happen if anyone found out. Life wouldn't be worth living.'

'No one will find out,' I assured him. We enjoyed being together in the grass, and started to caress each other in the simple way that boys do: fondling, kissing and saying silly things.

'You won't mention this to your friend, will you?' asked the handsome lad.'

'Oh sure! I'll tell every silly bugger! Here's the wonderful boy I've been following for weeks! He pulls your jock-strap down in the grass and plays with your dick in the open countryside. This is handsome Jackie Clithero! I love him, and I'm going to sling this fuckin' stripe tomorrow so that we can be together!'

'You're just as bad as me,' said Clithero with a laugh. 'Do you say things like that to Jamie Dunlop?'

'Things like what?' I asked, pulling the front of his tracksuit down and fondling his wonderful masculine warmth.

'I love you...stuff like that?'

'All the time,' I replied, kissing Jackie's rich red lips. 'Do you like it?'

'Mmmm!' he murmured shyly, 'but I couldn't imagine you saying things like that to another guy.'

'I love you,' I repeated with a smile on my face. 'It comes natural. How can you kiss someone if you don't care for them?'

'I think I care for you,' answered Clithero and kissed me with a simple boyish kiss. We didn't have full sex. It wasn't really necessary and I don't think we were prepared for it on our first date, but we knew it would take place some time in the future. We wanted each other.

Ejaculation can be a messy thing. However, the green grass

didn't seem to mind and my new friend wasn't embarrassed when we shared the beauty of our shooting stars. He knew it was for real and not just a sexy little game that some boys get involved in.

'I'll play something special for you,' Clithero said as he jogged by my side. 'You'll hear it when I sound the Last Post. I'm on guard duty tomorrow night.'

'You can't do that,' I replied as we joined up with a stream of runners heading for Maida Barracks. 'You can't fuck about with the Last Post. The bloody notes have got to be the same every time.'

'Not when I play,' answered the smiling boy. 'I'm going to tell the whole fuckin' regiment that I've found someone at last. I love you, Jackie boy!'

'And me, Jackie boy!'

'I'll call you Lance Jack,' he said. 'Crazy! Fancy both of us having the same bloody name.'

'When do we meet again?' I asked as we crossed the barrack square.

'Tonight in the gym. I'm eighteen and can do as I like. So long Lance Jack.'

'So long, Jackie! See you tonight.'

Old Billy was about 35 years old and had been middleweight champion of India. His brother Tommy was the army cruiserweight champion and his other brother, Johnny, had retired after 21 years as the undefeated heavyweight champion of the army and bought a tattooist shop outside the castle at Chester, the home of the regiment.

Billy smoothed my bare shoulders with his hands. 'You're fuckin' beautiful!' he said through his broken nose. 'Why don't you box for the battalion? You move like a fuckin' dream. You've got a lot to learn, but believe me, kid, I could make a champion out of you.'

I smiled and relaxed beneath the pressure of his wonderful hands. Billy could seek out a ruptured blood vessel, straighten out a kinky back and bring a paralysed muscle back to life. 'I bet you say that to all the boys,' I quipped sarcastically.

Billy pulled the towel from my bottom. 'Turn over,' he asked. 'Jesus! You could give it a six-month trial.' He put the towel over my front and massaged my chest with his special hands.

'I'm not interested,' I said when he asked me again.

'Then what the hell do you train for?' asked the punchy old boxer, taking the deltoids in his fingers and sliding his hands down my arm.

'I like boxing,' came the reply. 'I don't intend to take a fuckin' hammering. I just like boxing. I've been doing it all my life.'

'Waste of a fuckin' good boxer,' he said turning to Clithero.

'Wanna rub down, kid?' Clithero stepped out of his knickers.

'Thanks, Billy,' he said in his fine boyish voice. 'Wait for me, Lance Jack. See you in the showers.' Jackie squirmed beneath the hands, and I wondered if Billy really did say that to all the boys.

'Still feel the same?' asked Clithero in the steam of the spartan shower room.

'Always will,' I replied. 'I don't make many friends, Jack, but when I do it's for keeps. Okay?'

He looked at the open door. Punchy Billy was leaning over a young kid on the rubbing-down bench. We heard his nasal voice clearly. 'You got style!' he was telling the kid. 'Jesus Christ! With triceps like them, you wanna be throwin' the javelin for the Olympic mob.'

Jackie leaned into me and kissed my cheek quickly.

'Let's try for a weekend pass,' he said. 'We could catch a train to London and stay at the YMCA.'

Someone was liable to walk in on us at any moment so we washed, rinsed away the rubbing oils and foul-smelling liniment and said goodbye. 'Don't forget to listen to the Last Post. So long, Lance Jack!' were his parting words.

The company sergeant-major sat in his office. 'I want to revert to the rank of private soldier,' I asked respectfully. 'How do I go about it, sir?'

'You'll have to see the RSM,' replied the daft old bugger. 'You are his blue-eyed boy! He made you and he can break you. I can't interfere. What's wrong? Young NCOs don't chuck their stripes away for nothing. Are the old Indian soldiers giving you a hard time?'

'No sir,' I answered. 'It's nothing like that.'

'What is it then?' asked the CSM. 'Perhaps I can help.'

'I've got no friends,' I answered quietly. 'I had a good pal when we came down here, and now I can't even have a cup of tea with him in the canteen.'

'Make friends with the other NCOs,' said the CSM. 'You don't want to be a private all your life, do you?'

'Not really, sir,' I remarked thoughtfully.

'What was your friend's name,' he asked.

'Dunlop, sir. He was your clerk until he became a batman to one of the mess officers.'

'Young Dunlop,' repeated the CSM. 'Got a head on him, that boy. He's applied for OTC. I'd forget about him, lad. He'll be in the officers' training corps before long, and he has the makings of a fine young lieutenant. Don't do anything foolish, son. Christ Almighty! You can meet your friends after duty, go to the garrison cinema, boxing, swimming, football. Holy Jesus! I couldn't even mix with my own brother when I was in India. The modern army treats you well! Best butter on the breakfast table. Jesus! It took me three years to get my first stripe and I didn't even get paid for it! I was an unpaid lance-corporal. You don't know you're born!'

'I want to see the RSM about chucking in my stripe,' I said stubbornly.

'Don't,' replied the simple old soldier. 'Think it over for a week or two. Dis...miss!'

It looked like Jamie was gone forever. I couldn't quite make up my mind, and as the silly stripe didn't affect Clithero and me as yet, I relaxed and listened to the voice of experience.

'Flash Gordon!' read the sign outside the garrison cinema. 'Flash Gordon shown in twelve separate parts! Episode Three showing all week!' I paid threepence for a seat in the back stalls and sat among the lovely boys in kilts.

Soldiers had two uniforms, a service dress or S.D. uniform, and a suit of brown denim or canvas, known as fatigues or undress uniform. The Highland soldier dressed in much the same way but he wore a kilt instead of trousers. The S.D. kilt was made of beautiful heavy tartan plaid, and the undress uniform kilt was a thin khaki-coloured skirt — flat and without the heavy pleats and little extras normally associated with the magnificent dress kilt.

The feature film was reasonable. I sat through Flash Gordon twice, and watched excitedly as lovely youngsters sat close and comfy, thin cotton skirts up around their thighs and sneaky little hands caressing sexy legs and standing erections. They were normal healthy boys, I suppose, although I suspect the lads in the back row were extra healthy. They were definitely young and beautiful! A lot were boys like myself. It was obvious.

The place reminded me of my early childhood and the 'Penny Lytton': peanut shells all over the carpets, orange peel and noisy lads. I quite expected someone to come bustling down the aisles shouting: 'Keep quiet!'

Boys kept swapping seats, shouting to their friends across the way, and running in and out of the toilets in a steady stream. I hadn't taken much notice in the past. Clithero's words, however, stuck in my childish mind: 'You can always find a nice boy at the garrison cinema.'

He was right! It crawled with gorgeous lads seeking a partner for the night or perhaps a permanent relationship. It was all friendly fun and games, but I was happy with Jackie Clithero and knew I'd found my dream boy at long last.

A dark-eyed beauty winked at me. 'Let me pass,' he asked in a soft lilting voice. 'I'm going for a pee.'

The gorgeous creature deliberately stumbled and almost sat his kilt-clad bottom on my knee before I could stand. 'Sorry,' he said, giving me another boyish wink. His pink cheeks glowed with wholesome health, sparkling little devils shone from his big round eyes, white even teeth glittered in the darkened cinema and he smelled of peach-flavoured bubblegum. What could I do? I was a normal, healthy, homosexual boy, and he was a most alluring, tempting young angel. I simply had to follow.

The pink-faced soldier boy raised his kilt with both hands and peed.

'Don't you wear shorts?' I asked the beautiful lad.

'Not when I come to the "Garry"!' he replied in his lilting Scottish accent. We held each other's stiffened sex and smiled.

'I must go,' I said nervously. 'I'm scared.'

'Please,' he whispered softly. 'I've been watching you all night. You want someone too, I can tell. Quickly! We can use a cubicle. Don't be afraid.' It was all over in a few exciting minutes; his light fawn kilt up around his trim young waist and my stiffened penis up his delightful young body. He ejaculated as I filled him with my shooting stars.

'See you for Chapter Four,' he said as we kissed and parted.

'Chapter Four?' The lovely youngster adjusted his kilt on the way out. 'Flash Gordon, Chapter Four, Saturday night. I never miss it,' he shouted over his shoulder. He returned to the back row, put his fine young arm around his friend's shoulder and they giggled like naughty boys in school. But they were professional soldiers...

The moon came out as I made my way to Maida Barracks, shining its pale beam across the barrack square and making me feel guilty as I thought of my friend Clithero on guard duty.

The Last Post is a beautiful piece of music. It incorporates many traditional calls, blends them together and ends the solider's day on a soft sad note. 'Just for you, Jackie boy,' I heard the bugle say.

'Christ!' said dreamy eyes. 'That must be Jackie Clithero. I've never heard anything so beautiful! Did you notice anything different about it, corporal?'

'Yeah!' I replied. 'Like he had a song in there..."Danny Boy", or something like that.'

'That was it!' said dreamy eyes. 'That was it — "O Danny boy, I love you so"!'

'Bullshit!' shouted Andy Lee. 'The Last Post is the fackin' Last

Post! I've been hearing it every night for ten fackin' years! It's always the same. "Danny Boy"! "Danny Boy"!, my fackin' arse! Get some service in...fackin' red-arse! You shoulda bin in India. The fackin' bugler used to stick his head outa the winder, sound reveille and go back to sleep with his buddly chum.'

'Shit in it!' said a voice in the dark. That meant 'keep quiet' among the old-timers, so they settled down to sleep and I played with Jackie Clithero in my dreams.

The early morning sunshine danced across the granite chips of the barrack square, flashed across my sleepy eyes like a semaphore mirror and brought me to my senses.

'Gunsmoke?' asked a friendly voice in my ear.

'Thanks,' I said sleepily, giving the early caller my huge white pint mug. He filled it to the brim with scalding hot tea and moved on to the next guy's bed, carrying the 'gunsmoke' in a gleaming five-gallon bucket.

'The fackin' wogs used to give me a shave before they brought the gunsmoke in,' said the noisome voice of Andy Lee. 'My nappi wallah could shave me without waking me up. Jesus! I'll be glad when this fackin' outfit goes out to bleedin' Bombay!'

'And me,' remarked his fat friend. 'Remember when we shot through the railway station with our bayonets stickin' outa the fuckin' winder. Fuckin' 'ell! There was some blood on the friggin' platform that day.'

'Hyderabad!' said Andy.

'Don't be a cunt!' said the voice on his left. 'It was Landikotel. I think I chopped some fuckin' wog's head off!'

'Balls,' snorted Chalky White. 'It was Allahabad. We were on the way to Delhi. I remember poking out the bayonets at every fuckin' station along the way.

'Who cares?' remarked Andy Lee. 'It was only a crowd of fackin' wogs an' half-chats!'

'Wicked bastards!' remarked young dreamy eyes, sipping at his scalding tea.' You should have been court-martialled.'

'Get some fuckin' service in!' shouted the ignorant old soldiers. 'Fackin' red-arse!'

I hated them. They didn't seem human, treated everyone with the utmost disrespect and despised anyone who was not pure white. Many soldiers had married overseas; their offspring joined the army and they were all called 'darkie'. Blackie Evans was a Welshman, but his mother had been part Indian. He looked a fine young soldier but because of the mixed marriage he was always known as Blackie.

The old soldiers wouldn't accept my youth and tried to ignore me. They were skilled gunners but were used to pack mules and couldn't accept the machine-guns going into action from motor transport. 'By the time we get the fuckin' tailboard down, we'll all be fuckin' shot to bleedin' pieces,' they complained. I stuck it out until the weekend, thinking I should pack in my stripe and hoping I would never serve in India.

A long weekend pass starts at 4 p.m. Friday.Clithero met me at the guard room, picked up his pass and waited for me by the sentry box. He was dressed in regimental blues: a gold filigree drum embroidered on his sturdy shoulder and a tiny bugle stitched to his forearm.

'You're a handsome bastard!' I said admiring him. 'I thought you'd be in civvies.'

He just smiled and said, 'Hiya, Lance Jack.' We caught the train at Station Road and rattled along the rails to London.

The Union Jack Club, a dilapidated Victorian building designed for servicemen on leave, was situated near Waterloo Station. I didn't like the look of it. Young Grenadiers in all their splendour, army reserves in sloppy battledress, pink-faced Jack Tars in bright blue number ones hung around the iron-railed steps, cigarettes drooping from the lip, fag ends behind the ear.

'I don't fancy this, Jackie. We might as well be in Aldershot.'

Clithero smiled.

'Let's try the YMCA,' he said. 'If that's no good we can stay in a cheap hotel. Okay?'

'Whatever you say.'

What a difference! The YMCA sparkled, a barrow full of fruit outside the revolving door, busy shoppers passing to and fro, fresh-faced youths in the comfortable lounge and a friendly guy on duty at the reception desk.

Clithero took the initiative. 'We'd like to stay until Monday,' he said.

'Is this your first time in the big city?' asked the clerk.

'Yes', said Clithero. 'We want to see the sights, the changing of the guard.'

The clerk gave us a street guide, a list of interesting shows, theatre programmes and a tiny card with the map of the underground in blue and red print.

'Would you like to share a room?' he enquired, tapping the desk wih a pen.

Jackie Clithero said yes, making my heart beat faster.

'Third floor,' said the guy at the desk. 'Here's two keys. Lock your room and hand them in when you go out.'

'What time do you close?'

'We don't. There's a man on duty all night.'

The room was neat and clean, a real luxury compared to the long cold dormitories of barrack-room life. Colourful curtains draped the windows, matching the gaily designed bedspreads and making the place look warm and cosy.

Clithero slung his bag on one of the beds. 'What should we do? Go to a show? Walk around the city?'

'I don't mind what we do. Let's go out. We'll find something interesting.'

I wanted to hold his hand in the lift. A magic, attractive magentism drew me to the boy and sent my heartstrings zinging. The lift stopped at the ground floor. We reached out to open the criss-crossed iron gate and felt our fingers touch. It was electrifying, made us jump. Then Jackie opened the old-fashioned door and we stepped outside to meet the London life.

Down Old Compton Street we went, side by side, blazing lights and cafes all around. Down Greek Street and Frith Street, shabby-looking men seeking an hour's work and a meal at Joe Lyons, brassy-looking prostitutes seeking a few bob in exchange for a poke and a free dose of clap.

Under the trees at Leicester Square painted young men hung around the lavatories. Smart young men in leather kneepads polished the shoes of the wealthy. Cherry Blossom uniforms on their bony backs, borough licence strapped to the forearm, Nugget and Kiwi signs on the tiny wooden footrests at the pavement's edge. 'Shine, sir.'

'How much?'

'Threepence.'

'Another time.'

'Thank you, sir'

Silk top hats, dancing pumps in gold and silver, diamond earrings, flashed beneath the night-club lights. Rolls and Daimler cars passed by. The Coventry Street AA man saluted them continually and smiled gratefully when his salutations were returned. Clever boy!

'Coming shortly: *Gone With The Wind.*'

'No charge for your second cup of coffee.

'*Mein Kampf* by Adolf Hitler. Europe's number 1 best-seller!'

'Let's have a look at the shows,' said my mate.

Tom Walls and Ralph Lynn...? 'I laughed till I cried' — *Evening Standard.*

Ivor Novello...'A sensitive performance' — *Daily Express.*

Windmill Theatre...'Girls, girls and more girls! — *The Times.*

There was more entertainment on the streeets. The cinema queues were lining up, buskers in the gutter, mouth organists, banjo-strumming music men and a one-legged lady on a crutch. She looked like an untidy washer-woman but sang like a highly trained opera singer and created a sensation with her silver tones and magic voice. The theatre crowd applauded, and the lady with the musical voice limped along and collected a few pennies.

The rattle of traffic on Coventry Street, the sound of rubber-bulbed taxi horns honking and hooting, three funny men on the white line — red, tasseled fezzes on their balding heads, blue and white striped gowns on their skinny frames, songs on their lips, sand dance at their twinkling toes...

Could they be Wilson, Kepple and Betty?

On with the dance!

The happy crowd of film fans moved along, throwing their spare coins and vanishing into the brightly lit foyers of the West End movie houses. The stars came out and said good evening to the silvery moon, but the blazing lights of Piccadilly put them in the shade.

Spaghetti bolognaise, hot and spicy, covered in grated Parmesan, served with a crusty chunk of French bread and washed down with a glass of rough red wine — fine fare for a couple of soldier boys on a weekend trip to the big smoke.

Onto the dusty sidewalk we went and into the cool September night, the sound of traffic in our ears and the city smells in our nostrils — hot chestnuts crackling, roasting on the coals, fumes from the brazier in our bright young eyes. Through the book-lined pavement of Charing Cross Road, tatty paperbacks, dusty brown shelves, hawkers, newsvendors, whores and pimps...

We were in the lift when Jackie put his hand round my waist, drew me close and saw my blushing face. 'It's alright,' he said gently. 'I knew in church. You want a big boy, don't you?'

'You don't mind?'

'You're a real sweetheart,' he said in our room. 'I thought you were after my bottom at first, but it's not like that, is it?'

'I'm sorry,' I said. 'Don't let it spoil our friendship.'

Jackie put a hand on my shoulder. 'Don't worry about it,' he said affectionately. 'I never had a friend like you. Pretty boys bother me. People talk.'

'I won't breathe a word, Jackie.'

His hands went round my back and pulled me close. Lips touched softly. I felt his kiss, a boy kiss. 'Do you want me to take your trousers down,' he asked sweetly.

'Not if it spoils our friendship,' I repeated, lips quivering, eyes a-flutter. 'Kiss me like that again, Jackie.'

He made a gasping sound, breathing hard, shaking at the knees.

'I want to fuck you!' he gasped. 'Let me stick it up your bottom. I've never done it to a boy.'

'In bed, Jackie. Do it in bed.'

'Now!' cried Clithero. 'Right now!'

Still shaky, he pulled my trousers down, raised my shirt tail, kissed my bare bottom. 'Whoo!' he gasped. 'You really want the dick. You're a girl! A real queenie boy.' He put his stiffness to mine, measured the length, rubbed the slippy tips together and gasped for breath.

'In bed! Take me to bed and fuck me, Jackie!'

Naked and stiff, he pushed himself into a jar of brylcreem and sucked his breath through parted lips. 'Can't breathe! Can't breathe!' he gasped.

'Don't get excited,' I said, taking his hand, stroking his thick dark hair. 'Take your time, Jackie. What's wrong?'

'Can't get my breath! Never done anything like this before!' He kissed my breast, sexy stiffness at my face, my chest, my bare bottom.

A couple of noisy youngsters banged their way along the thin-walled corridor.

'Just hold hands, Jackie. Take it easy,' I said. Brylcreem in his hairs, on my legs and slippy at my belly, I kissed the boy, pushed my tongue between his lips and made him gasp again.

'Aw! Whoo! Wheeh! You're really going to get it now!'

I put some more cream on him, used it on myself, took his strength inside me.

'Oh it's really there!' gasped the sexy lad. 'Whoo! Lift up a bit. Are you alright?'

'Mmmm! Just do it. Love me. Love me.'

'Jesus!' he blurted out. 'I can see it going in and out. I'm gonna die!'

'Hush, Jackie. Just make love to me.'

He sucked in his breath, blew it out, gasped in my ear.

'That's it!' he sighed. 'I'm fucking you, sweetheart. Oh I love it.'

'And me! Don't get too excited. Do it slowly.'

'It's gonna squirt! Gonna come! Gonna come right up you!'

I kissed his handsome face, felt him relax, stroked at his chest.

'Never done anything like that before, not a real fuck. God! Are you alright?' he asked tenderly.

'Yes, I'm happy,' I sighed, moving into his warm arms. 'Just hold me tight.'

'Have you had a dick up you before?'

'Yes, you know I have. It's the way I am. I need a boy like you.'

'Jamie Dunlop?' he asked. 'Was it Jamie?'

'No. He's like me. He doesn't do it.'

'Two girls?' asked Clithero. 'Two sweethearts? Two girlie boys?'

'Yes. Jamie's a nice kid. We just got parted, that's all. Do you still want me for your friend?'

Clithero squeezed my fingers. 'Of course I do. We're both the same. I want a good friend and I'm not interested in girls. Who was it? Who fucked you?'

'My school friend. He's like you, a homosexual boy.'

'Whoooo! I wish I wasn't so breathless. You're a lovely guy, girl, boy. I don't know what to call you. I'm not like that. You don't want to do it to me, do you?'

'No. I just want you to love me.'

'Do I have to kiss you?' he asked, nose to nose.

'If you like me.'

Clithero kissed my lips and shut me up.

The next morning Jackie felt my lips at his belly, in his warm hairs, on his exciting sex.

'Suck it!' he said, taking my head in his hands. 'I've never been sucked.'

I kissed the lovely thing.

'Please,' he whispered. 'I won't come in your mouth.'

'You will,' I replied. 'That's what I want, Jackie. I want to taste you. Suck you right off.'

He held me and I drank his sweetness down.

'Aw! Whoo!' Clithero gasped. 'That's it! You must think a lot of me, dear.'

'I think I love you,' I said quietly.

'You shouldn't call me "dear",' I said in the lift.

'Why not?' asked Clithero. 'You like all that lovey-dovey stuff.'

'It'll become a habit.'

'How about in bed?'

'If you can get your breath, handsome!'

He pinched my bottom and we went outside to find that war had been declared.

4. The Buildings

All my friends vanished overnight. Jamie, Duffy and Jackie Clithero, Rodney and even young Joey Meyers. The war just swallowed them up. No time for tears. I knew that one of them would write and contact me.

Meanwhile I was sent to Chester and given a new job as assistant squad commander. Thousands of young conscripts poured into the castle and I had to join the training team, knock them into shape, make them into soldiers. A few corporals, half a dozen sergeants and a couple of handsome young athletes from the Army School of Physical Training made up the rest of the team, and we got to work.

Training recruits came easy. Young conscripts, boys of twenty years, arrived at the castle in droves, spent six weeks in hell and went off to war as soldiers. Squad after squad passed through my hands, lovely youngsters, dragged from their homes and forced into a way of life they didn't want and couldn't understand. They were wonderful, took it all on the chin, never complained and simply wanted the stupid war to end so they could pick up what was left of their disrupted lives.

Great friendships were won and lost in a glorious spirit of comradeship and love. A second stripe brought a little extra pay and a saucy letter of congratulations from Jamie, the guy who never forgot. He must have seen the promotion in the regimental orders of the day. There was no address, but I guessed he was still in England.

The daily grind had left me with a swaggering self-confidence that bubbled over and contaminated those around me. It was a time of great madness. Boys came and went and showered me with gifts, tokens of friendship, presents for turning them into killers and cannon fodder.

Weekend passes were hard to come by, so I made my own and went to Liverpool every Saturday.

Bombs as big as telephone boxes fell from the night skies, killed thousands of innocent civilians and set Merseyside alight.

Outraged citizens demonstrated on the streets, complaining bitterly, but the madness went on and on. The propaganda machine labelled them Nazi sympathisers, and the war-mongers told them to shut up or be interned in the Isle of Man concentration camp. Millions of gas masks were issued, one specially designed for babies and old folk. 'Don't forget your gas mask!' was the slogan of the day. Public baths and wash-houses became decontamination centres and the recognised antidote for mustard gas victims was a wash down with undiluted bleach. Fortunately, Joe Public didn't know anything about this wonderful method of saving his life. He'd discover it when he got gassed.

If I'd had any sense, I'd have stayed away from Liverpool and remained in the safety and security of my comfortable military base in the countryside of Cheshire. However, the boozy parties and jazzy shindigs at Annie Jones' home in the 'Buildings' drew me to their friendly bosom week after week.

Stirrup pumps and buckets of water were positioned on the roof-tops. Mr and Mrs Liverpool, along with a few old-timers from the Home Guard, were obliged to take turns as fire-watchers, use the water and put out the incendiary bombs. Poor old Joe Public! They didn't tell him that water is the only dangerous thing to use on fire bombs — the action of H_2O on phosphorous and magnesium created more fires.

The wackers and judies of Liverpool slaved throughout the blazing nights, saving the warehouses and important city buildings for their wealthy owners. A few severe burns, some dirty faces and plenty of lovely smiles appeared on the front page of the *Daily Liar*: Britain Can Take It! The old propaganda machine could really go!

Housewives in suburban areas and families living in isolated country towns and villages were advised to keep an open pot of pepper handy and a pan of water boiling on the stove in case the enemy invaders appeared in the night. Ground pepper vanished from the stores and had to be replaced with a chemical known as pepper substitute. Christ knows who paid the inflated gas bills. Wave the jolly old flag, bang the friggin' drum, and Mr and Mrs Great Britain will swallow anything!

A lovely young singer named Vera Lynn sugared the pill for them with songs like 'White Cliffs of Dover', 'When the Lights Go On Again', and a number one hit from Germany: 'Lili Marlene'. They'd been singing 'We're Gonna Hang Out the Washing On the Siegfried Line', but they packed that up after the British Expeditionary Force left Dunkirk and reached the shores of Great Britain with wet trousers and no guns! It was called a great victory by the

Ministry of Information, and everyone believed it. The BSA and other arms manufacturers must have laughed up their made-to-measure sleeves, put the peasants on overtime and offered them a generous war bonus.

The new troops who were using broomsticks for rifle drill, and the guys in the Home Guard training with pikestaffs left over from Cromwell's forces, may have had doubts about the country's security, but they were easily seduced by a few witty cartoons in the *War Monger*.

'Dig for victory!' The city housewives planted cabbages in their window-boxes. Every military establishment in the countryside had a vegetable patch, and the anti-aircraft stations became market gardens overnight.

'Spam is full of nourishment!'

'Dried eggs are good for growing infants!'

'Powdered milk stays fresh!'

'Keep it dark. It's a black pudden!'

The Ministry of Information and Propaganda produced second-rate movies that depicted the Germans as sadistic robots with brutal methods of interrogation. They certainly knew the subject — every CID squad in the big cities of England had an interrogation room, and it was common practice for CID officers to almost beat a man to death. A suspected criminal could avoid brutal treatment at the hands of the CID if he made a written statement and gave evidence against himself. Floggings, canings, corporal punishment by the cat o' nine tails and execution at the hangman's noose were common practice in Merrie England, so I guess the Germans weren't the only uncivilised brutes in Europe.

Someone waved a magic wand and Jackie Clithero appeared on the barrack square. He was given a stripe, teamed up with me and became assistant squad commander. Things settled down after that. I loved Clithero sincerely. We worked hard and became a very dynamic team producing squad after squad of highly trained youngsters. God knows what happened to them. Jackie and I slept together every night and our love-making developed beautifully.

The castle was taken over by the women's army and we moved to a brand-new training establishment about three miles away. It was wonderful! A brand-new hospital, huge modern gymnasium and separate sanitation blocks stretched across the camp, with flower-beds placed between the warm and comfortable chalets. Concrete pathways ran from chalet to shower room, and you could roam the open countryside when off duty. Boys got up from their beds at night and walked to the showers and other modern conveniences in their shirt tails. Some kept little rendezvous in the steamy showers, naked and carefree. I loved it and hoped the war would last for ever.

Thousands of temporary YMCAs, Toc-H institutes and Salvation Army units sprang up like mushrooms all over the country. Every tiny railway station, country town and simple little village had a 'bed for the boys'. The Women's Institute or some other female organisation produced free tea and cakes. It seemed like the whole world wanted us, and the whole world was on the move...

Jackie leaned from his bunk and tousled my hair one morning. 'Wake up sleepy head,' said the lovely young man. 'You're taking me to Liverpool. Remember?'

Liverpool was only about twenty-five miles away. We had a ten-day pass and I'd promised Jackie a good time in the dirty old town.

Two military police stopped us at the railway station, checked our passes and asked where we were going.

'Liverpool,' answered Jackie.

'Take my advice,' said one of them. 'Spend your leave in Chester. Liverpool is being bombed to hell!'

Jackie had never had a decent holiday in his life. We'd shared a few weekend passes together but this was absolutely out of this world! A ten-day pass was a gift from the gods.

'Balls!' snorted Jackie as we got aboard the train. 'I've never been to Liverpool. Let's go, kid!'

The train was packed from end to end with bright-eyed servicemen of all nationalities: Polish guys in strange-looking hats, gold-capped teeth agleam, Frenchmen smoking foul-smelling cigarettes, Yankee soldiers chewing gum, beautifully tailored tight trousers flattering their well-shaped bodies and neat little bottoms, chests drenched with childish medals — one for crossing the Atlantic, one for firing a rifle, one for wearing on Sundays, one for striking matches on and probably one for eating Hershey bars and ice-cream. Nevertheless, I liked the US servicemen. They had a wonderful modern way about them and made jokes about their silly decorations.

We got off the train in Liverpool and walked down the platform rubbing shoulders with gorgeous brylcreemed boys, all wavy-haired and fragrant.

'This is the house,' I said to my friend as we reached the tenements. 'They'll put us up and make us welcome. You'll have a friggin' marvellous time!'

We knocked with the rusty iron door-knocker. A window opened in the house next door. 'Who's there?' asked a voice at the window.

'Friends of Mrs Jones,' I replied.

'There's nobody in,' answered the voice. 'What do you want?'

'We want to get drunk and sing and dance all night!' I shouted. 'Rosie and Anne are my friends. They often put me up. I used to work at Mrs Jones's stall on Paddy's market. Jimmy knows me. I used to sing in the choir with him.'

'Jimmy's missing at sea,' replied the voice. 'You must be young Jackie. Come inside. I'll make you a cup of tea.'

The door made a creaking noise and an old lady appeared.

'Let's clear off!' Clithero said quietly. 'I don't like all this.'

'Eh? What's that?' asked the old dear.

'My friend's a bit shy,' I explained. 'He's never been in Liverpool before.'

'In you go,' said the old lady. 'Put three teaspoons of tea in the pot,' she added, poking Jackie in the ribs with a bony finger. 'You'll find everything you want in the kitchen.'

The house was spotless.Three sheets of newspaper covered the living-room table. 'I suppose I'd better put a tablecloth on, or Annie Jones will be afer me,' she mumbled.

'Don't mind us,' I said grinning all over my face. She peeled the tea-stained *Liverpool Echo* from the table and replaced it with a heavy, embroidered tablecloth, tasselled and hanging almost to the floor.

Clithero came in from the kitchen. 'Where shall I put the tray?' he asked.

She looked at the hand-made cloth. It really was beautiful and must have been one of her most treasured possessions. 'Just a minute,' she said decisively, and put a clean newspaper on top of the lovely cloth. 'Stick it on the *Echo*,' she said at last.

Jackie put a black and gold japanned tray on the newspaper. It was elegant; varnished and embellished with raised figures, a work of art and craftsmanship long gone.

'My son brought me that from Yokohama,' she said proudly.

Clithero put a little milk in the delicate china cups, poured the tea from a small fat-bellied pot and passed a pair of silver sugar tongs to the old lady.

'Never touch it,' she said with a wink. 'I've pounds and pounds of sugar in the house, and no one else has got a spoonful!'

She enjoyed talking about the neighbours. Under normal circumstances, we would probably have left the old dear and returned later. However, she made us so very welcome that it seemed unfair.

'Rosie and Anne work in the American Tobacco Company,' she

informed us. 'They'll be home shortly. Mrs Jones will get home soon after the girls and God only knows when the old man will get home. He works at the docks and they've been on fire for two days and nights.'

'What happened to Jimmy?' I asked.'

'Jesus, Mary and Joseph!' exclaimed the shawl-clad woman. 'Don't mention it to Annie. He's missing...that's all we know.'

A knock came at the door. It was young Tony Campello and his mate. Tony put a bottle of brandy on the sideboard. 'All the way from New York,' he said. 'That's for you, Ma. Tell Mrs Jones I'll be round for a booze-up tonight. I've just paid off the *Mary*.' He looked into the mirror, adjusted his wide-brimmed stetson and gave me the 'hi' sign: hand raised level with his ear, index finger and thumb forming a circle, and the other three fingers pointing up at the ceiling.

'Hi!' I replied. 'Long time no see, Tony.'

He pulled his overcoat collar up. 'See you tonight,' he said, giving a passable impersonation of James Cagney. 'My brothers and all Jimmy's uncles are coming round. So long, Robbo!' He grabbed the old lady round the waist, performed a few jazzy dance steps and kissed her on the forehead. 'Don't drink it all at once,' he said as he went out of the door.

'Lovely boy!' remarked the old dear. 'Voice like an angel. Every time he comes home from sea he brings me a present.'

'Is he your grandson?' Clithero enquired.

'Good heavens, no!' she replied. 'The Campellos are Italians! My husband used to sail on the China boats with Tony's father. All the Campello boys are on the *Queen Mary*. My lad sails with the Blue Funnel Line and he's away for years on end, but the *Mary* docks every fortnight.'

That little bit of information was supposed to explain everything. However, Jackie and I were not familiar with the brotherhood of the seas, and accepted it for what it was worth. Tony was the youngest of the Campello family. He was not yet seventeen. I remembered the beautiful boy singing in the choir of St Francis Xavier; he was always chosen for a solo. I hoped he would sing for us tonight when everyone got drunk.

Clithero washed the cups, put a couple of sugar lumps in his mouth and put the tray back where he'd found it. Familiar voices came from the house next door.

'The girls must be home,' remarked the old lady. 'Oh dear! It sounds like Annie Jones's voice.'

'She whipped the newspaper from the table, folded it and shoved it in a little fireside box; a kind of metal box-like fender with a padded seat. Sticks of firewood were kept in the box and small lumps of coal were kept in an identical padded twin at the opposite side of the fireplace. Jackie raised the lid of the twin, picked up a gleaming steel fireside shovel and banked up the flames in the grate. He seemed very much at home, willing to please and thankful for the old lady's pleasant hospitality.

Rosie-Anne Jones was the toughest woman I knew. She could put the strongest man down with a quick movement of the hand and foot, almost like a judo expert. God knows where she learned to handle herself. When she got mad and offered her hand in apparent friendship, watch out! You went flat on your back screaming with pain, and usually finished up with a broken thumb.

Names can be a bloody mix-up and Mrs Jones certainly created that. Her husband's name was Jimmy, her son's name was Jimmy and the daughters were Rosie and Anne. Mr Jimmy Jones sat in his armchair reading the *Liverpool Echo*, two days' growth of beard on his unwashed face and burn marks on his navy-blue overalls. He smelt of fire and his hair was singed. Anne, the younger, more demure and feminine of the sisters, smilingly removed our coats and hung them up for us. Rosie sat on a couch painting her toenails.

'Jackie Robbo!' she said, pointing a foul-smelling nail-varnish brush at me. 'Are you staying?'

'If you'll have me,' I replied.

Mrs Jones came in from the kitchen, hugged me tight and said, 'You can stay as long as you like, dear. Who's your friend?'

'His name's Jack,' I said when I got my breath back. We've got a ten-day pass.'

'Jesus!' remarked Mr Jones. 'Another Jack. How are you, lads?'

'Great,' came the reply. 'You look as if you've been in a fire.'

'Wait till seven o'clock tonight,' he said. 'They'll be back at seven. I wouldn't be surprised if the whole bloody town went on fire.'

He stuck his nose back in the *Echo*.

Mrs Jones put her arms around Clithero. 'Jesus, Mary and Joseph!' she cried. 'Look after my Jimmy!'

'He'll be alright,' said the old man. ' "Missing" means they don't know where he is. Now, if it was "lost at sea"...'

'Put the bloody *Echo* down and get washed!' shouted his wife. 'Lost at sea...lost at sea...Holy Mary Mother of God!' She wiped a pinafore across her cheek, and went into the kitchen to make some ham sandwiches for the 'do'.

A 'do' is a crowd of people, drinking, singing, dancing, eating ham sandwiches and pissing against the backyard wall. The women make the sandwiches, hundreds of cups of tea, pay for the ale and never seem to go for a pee.

Two big guys walked into the house. They were much older than me and Jackie. One shoved two bottles of whisky on the sideboard and the other put his fat bottom on the settee.

'Watch it!' shouted Rosie. 'You're an awkward bugger, Uncle Jim. Now look what you've done!'

'Are you going jazzin'?' asked her fat uncle.

'Not tonight,' answered Roise. 'I'm going to the alehouse with everyone else.'

'Not me,' said dainty Annie Jones.

'Oooh dear,' remarked Rosie. 'Listen to Polly Flinders.'

Tony Campello and his brothers walked in like American gangsters, piled the sideboard with bottles of rum, whisky and Guinness, looked into the mirror over the fireplace, pulled their stetsons over one eye and went into the kitchen. Mrs Jones struggled with them, but they managed to persuade her to put her coat on. It seemed to be the signal for everyone to leave.

'The alehouse is open,' said Jimmy Malone and raised his fat bottom from the settee. The other big guy, his brother Tom, grabbed Rosie and we all filed out to the nearest boozer.

Young Tony walked between me and Clithero. 'Let's get oiled up,' he said like an experienced old soak and linked arms with us. There were about twenty people in the party. Most of them walked the pavement, arms linked in threes and fours until we reached the pub.

A Liverpool 'do' starts in a pub. Everyone gets oiled up and somebody calls for order by banging on a table with a beer bottle. 'One singer! One song!' shouts the bottle banger and some silly fool gets up to give a song. Naturally, you can only get oiled up if there is a piano in the boozer and, most important, a good pianist.

Marty Campello wanted to sing 'The Darktown Strutters' Ball' but the old bag at the piano didn't know it.

'I do,' said Clithero and seated himself at the keyboard.

'Order please!' shouted the bottle banger. An Irishman sang 'I'll Take You Home Again Kathleen'. He had a wonderful voice — you could smell the fresh green fields and almost feel the ocean . . . wide and wild. All the old biddies started crying in their Guinness and when the guy finished singing, a dozen bottles of Guinness piled up on the piano for him.

Clithero started laughing. He opened the back of the piano, shoved a sheet of newspaper down the soft felt hammers and strings, and played the most amazing boogie-woogie, with a strange clicking sound coming from the paper sheet. Everyone applauded. I felt proud when Jackie handed the piano back to the original pianist.

'Thank you,' she said, and downed two bottles of the Irishman's Guinness before you could say Jack Robinson.

Jimmy Jones looked at Tony's gold watch. 'They're late tonight,' he said over the bar-room table.

'Who's late?' asked Jackie Clithero.

'The friggin' bombers,' said the old man in reply. 'They should have been over hours ago.'

'Two beers upstairs!' called a loud voice. 'And one for the pianist.' It just went on and on . . . sad songs, new songs, old songs and the inevitable 'Maggie May'. After closing, dozens of people traipsed over to the house, carrying bottles and cases of every description, and the 'do' began in earnest. The big stout uncles sang 'We Are The Brothers Malone', Clithero played the piano and the bombs began to drop.

'Anyone for the air-raid shelter?' shouted Mr Jimmy Jones. Nobody took a blind bit of notice. The old man sat by the fire and stuck his nose in the *Echo*. Tony Campello went next door and got the old lady. I was dancing with dainty Annie Jones when the whisper went around, 'Jimmy's home . . . Jimmy's home!' Jimmy threw his kit bag on the living-room floor, his sailor's hat on his dad's head and his arms around his mum.

'Holy Mary Mother of God!' shouted the delighted woman and danced all round the house with her handsome sailor boy. Mr Jones stuck his nose deeper in the *Echo*. The sailor's hat didn't have a peak to hide his tears.

Drunken Liverpudlians at a 'do' don't mind what kind of song you sing, as long as you can sing. If you're good they applaud, but if you're bad they shout, 'Sit down for Christ's sake, and give your arse a chance.' Mrs Jones was no more religious than the rest of the hard-drinking mob. However, she asked Tony Campello to sing 'Ave Maria'. Possibly she was thanking God in her own little way.

Tony stood at the piano and Jackie played while the boy sang in Latin. His wonderful sweet voice had not broken. Everyone froze as the choirboy voice filled the room with beauty. Clithero broke down in tears, left the piano and joined Rosie and me on the settee.

'What's wrong?' I enquired.

'Leave him alone,' said Rosie. 'He's crying drunk! Everyone gets crying drunk at times.'

'Jesus Christ!' blasphemed Clithero when he recovered. 'I've never known anything like it. Crazy people, bombs dropping all over the place, half the town's on fire, and nobody gives a fuck!'

'Die if you worry, die if you don't,' said the old lady from next door. 'Come on, son. Let's have a waltz.'

They waltzed away, the brothers Malone sang a very rude Liverpool song and that's about the last thing I remember of the actual party. The tough market trader bundled Jackie and me into the front room, pulled down the familiar old bed-settee and threw a couple of pillows on it. 'You'll be alright in here,' she said in her rough and ready way. 'God bless you, lads.'

There was an old-fashioned pianola in the room: a player piano that works when you press the foot pedals. We undressed. Jackie sat at the pianola in his knickers and worked the pedals. The black and white keys went up and down as if by magic and an old tune came pounding out: 'She is the lily of Laguna . . . She is my lily and my rose . . .'

'What a fuckin' night!' Jackie shouted. 'Jesus! I shoulda brought my fuckin' trumpet!' He put out the lights and dived into the warm bed with me. Bombs crumped and crunched nearby as we held hands. Some members of the party went out to the air-raid shelter, a huge communal one for the whole tenement block.

'Do you want to join the others in the shelter?' I asked.

'Piss off!' replied my friend. 'The first time we've ever been in a double-bed and you ask me a question like that.' We kissed and cuddled down, then a thunderous noise scared the life out of us.

'Do you want to go to the shelter?' asked Jackie.

'I'm not sure,' I said, 'but I think I'll put my knickers on.'

The noise rattled the windows and the whole building seemed to shake.

'Don't be scared!' shouted the voice of Mr Jones. 'It's the anti-aircraft train. It'll be all over in a minute!'

God knows what the anti-aircraft train was — some kind of mobile secret weapon — but it scared us more than the bombs. The all clear sounded and we made love, Jackie filling me with happiness.

There were people sleeping all over the place when we awoke. Sweet Anne put a cup of tea in our hands. Young Tony walked into the kitchen and joined us. He looked absolutely breathtaking in his snow-white shirt and charcoal-grey slacks. Anne gave the gorgeous young creature a cup of tea. 'Would you like some breakfast?' she asked the handsome choirboy. 'I'll take the boys out to a cafe. If we get stuck into your grub, we'll eat you out of house and home.'

'Suit yourself,' Anne replied. 'We've got plenty of food in the house. Mum makes sure we don't go short.'

Tony drank his tea, put his expensive-looking coat on and adjusted his stetson in front of the mirror. It changed him from beautiful youth to tough-looking seafarer. 'Let's go!' he said like George Raft. 'You guys got appetites, ain't ya?'

The city was a smoking ruin; broken glass, hosepipes and fire-fighters everywhere. We went into a joint called the City Milk Bar. 'What ya got, sweetheart?' said Tony to the girl behind the counter.

'Spam fritters,' replied sweetheart.

He flashed his merchant navy badge and gave her a long slow wink. 'What ya got for a guy off the *Queen Mary* with a dozen pairs of nylons in his pocket?'

'Bloody liar!' said sweetheart.

'Look,' teased the handsome boy and flashed a flimsy packet of nylons in front of sweetheart's nose.

'Spam fritters, fried eggs, baked beans and real sugar in the coffee,' she answered with a smile on her pretty face.

Tony put the nylons on the counter. 'Three times!' he ordered. 'Lots of sugar in the coffee, baby!'

He didn't know he was funny, and he was so very beautiful that I couldn't possibly laugh at him. I think Clithero took him seriously, but all I wanted was to take him in my arms and make love to him.

The second do started in much the same way as the first, Clithero taking over the piano when we reached the house. He was very popular and it was expected of him because he was such a good pianist.

The bombers came over dead on time. This was terrifying, huge land-mines as big as telephone boxes coming down out of the skies on parachutes. A nearby department store caught a direct hit and the whole city shook. Air-raid wardens chased the local residents into the huge brick and concrete shelters. 'We'd better get out!' declared the old man. 'We can finish the do in the shelter.'

Everybody carried some booze, and the party went on from there. The brothers Malone were the life of the party. Music was provided by an accordion, and instead of pissing against the backyard wall they pissed beneath the fingers of the searching bright lights. It was quite a change, but just a little scary.

The all clear sounded but they were having so much fun that most of the relieved merry-makers decided to stick it out until they ran out of booze. Meanwhile Jackie and I undressed in the comfortable front room and dived into bed. Young Tony, with whom I had passed a friendly hour during the early part of the evening, came into our room with Mrs Jones.

'Can you squeeze a little one in there?' asked the tough market trader. 'The house is full.'

'Jump in!' said Jackie naturally. Mrs Jones rumpled Tony's nice black hair and the boy slipped out of his jacket. I kept my fingers crossed, watched the lovely young sailor boy strip down to his candy-striped knickers and hoped he'd sleep beside me. I was in luck. He switched off the lights and slid between the sheets.

'Goodnight,' I said to Jackie, squeezing his hand. 'See you in the morning.'

Clithero returned the squeeze. He'd been well oiled in the air-raid shelter and soon fell asleep.

Tony didn't seem to mind when my hand rested on his trim young waist. His dark black hair smelled fragrant and his bronzed, warm skin felt smooth and delightful on my chest. His tough attitude and masculine seafarer's ways prevented me from tagging him as one of my own kind; as yet he was simply a bed-mate, although the most fragrant one by far.

Tony's candy-striped knickers were American designed and had a little opening with a button at the top. His legs were warm and close. I put my knees into his and moved closer, knickers touching his cotton-clad bottom. There was nothing I could do about it. You can't put a donkey in a bed of strawberries and not expect him to eat the whole damn lot.

The boy stirred. My cheek rested lightly on his shoulder-blades. The delicious aroma of pure boy entered my nostrils and I knew instinctively that he was one of my kind. Perhaps he would not like me physically. Just how he would react I knew not, but no power on earth could have kept me from trying. I could quite easily feign sleep if he objected.

The gentle boy seemed to be sleeping. The heat from his lovely body burned into my lower abdomen, making my hardened penis throb with desire. It was so beautiful I hardly moved. How could I find out if he wanted me? My little finger slid into the opening in his shorts, the other fingers resting lightly on the cotton pants and my thumb on the exasperating button. Was he sexually excited? Soft hairs touched my little finger. I remained perfectly still, steel-hard sex pressed against him, giving him the message. It was heavenly.

The boy moved very slightly and his stiff little erection touched my finger. He moved again, I pushed harder. Tony pushed back firmly so I kissed his shoulders and placed my hand fair and square on his swollen little knickers. He grew much harder as I fumbled with the tiny button at his waist.

It was done; the stiffened young sex throbbed in my hand and he made a sleepy boyish sound. I froze. Tony moved very slowly, his erect and tensile penis springy between a circle of my thumb and forefinger.

I wondered how far he was prepared to go. The beautiful thing slid in and out of the circled hold. He pushed it to the limit and remained still, his soft immature bushy hair close up to my palm.

He raised his hip slightly as I tugged his candy-striped knickers down to his knees. The Warsaw Concerto kept going through my mind, ridiculous music at a time like this. Perhaps I was feeling guilty. Clithero had been playing the beautiful piece of music all night long; it was just as popular as a modern dance tune and on everybody's lips. The Warsaw Concerto was meant to be played on the piano, and a skilled musician like Jackie could produce the sounds of the bombs, explosions and rat-a-tat-tat of machine-guns.

Tony sighed, moved his legs and kicked away his pants with his foot. The Warsaw Concerto vanished from my mind and I pulled my own knickers down. Tony moved in and out of my fingers again, slowly, deliberately, and obviously enjoying the wonderful sensations almost as much as me. I was afraid of disturbing Jackie, so I left my knickers round my ankles. Tony hooked his big toe into them, gave a little kick and sent them to the foot of the bed to rest with his own sweet-smelling shorts. 'Perhaps he'll go all the way,' I thought and placed my slippy erection where I thought he needed it most.

He sighed with sleepy pleasure and took an inch of tensile flesh inside him. You could hardly call it an entrance, but it was sufficient to pass the shooting seeds into him if that was what he wanted. If he needed any more it was there for him. However, I was quite satisfied and would not have hurt the delightful young choirboy for the world.

My lips kissed gently at his warm skin. He got very excited, took my hand from the magic wand and placed it on his boyish breast. I fondled his little nipple and pushed a fraction more penis into him. Tony placed my hand round his stiff young erection and moved very fast. He wet my fingers with slippy seed. The warm fluid excited me and sent my own fluid into the gorgeous boy. We shuddered, held tight until the magic was spent and he turned in my arms. Our lips met like lovers. I knew I would seek a beautiful boy like this for the rest of my life and never find one so absolutely perfect.

He slept like a baby in my embrace. Somehow, I managed to slip his little pants up around his bottom, struggle into my knickers and kiss his sweet red lips before sleep crept up on me and closed my eyes, the Warsaw Concerto still pounding away in my brain.

'Tea up!' said a happy girlish voice in my ear. Rosie Jones sat on the edge of our bed in her nightie. She had three cups of tea that rattled on the tin tray in her painted fingers.

Tony seemed very much at ease with girls. 'Hi baby!' he said like Humphrey Bogart. 'Pass my pants, willya?'

Rosie put the tray down and threw his trousers to the cheeky lad. He climbed out of bed, slipped his trousers on and sat at the player piano to drink his tea.

'I like your sexy American shorts,' remarked Rosie. 'Did you bring any for me?'

'Nylons, full-sets, silky blouses and titty bags with pads in,' came the surprising reply.

'Cheeky bugger,' giggled Rosie. 'Honestly Tony, you say the most shocking things for a boy of your age. Have they really got pads in?'

'If you let me feel your tits, I'll know what size to give you,' responded the lad.

'Tony!'

'Take it easy, babe. I gotta grip full of nylons for you and your sister.' He plonked his empty cup on the tray. Rosie kissed him on the cheek and disappeared.

It was quite late in the day. We washed beneath the kitchen tap. Mrs Jones shoved thick bacon sandwiches in our hands, and cups of tea laced with brandy.

'There's a big do at our house tonight,' said Tony with his mouth full. 'Who's coming?'

'Everyone,' shouted Rosie. 'But I want my nylons first. I'm fed up with painted legs.'

'Me too,' added her dainty sister. 'Have you got any nylons for me, Tony?'

'Betcha life, kid. Come to my room and try them on,' he said impudently. Mrs Jones came at him with her hand outstretched. Tony grabbed his stetson and fled.

'I've never seen a boy change so much,' said Rosie-Anne Jones. 'He used to be such a sweet little lad — now he's up to his eyes in the black market. It's going to sea that does it.'

A 'big do' is something special; a celebration, wedding or big family gathering. The Mary Ellens leave their high-button boots and shawls at home, dress in the height of fashion, and even take a bath.

Mr Campello had left the sea and worked as a chef in one of the city's big hotels. God knows why he threw the 'big do', but it must have been an important occasion, because young Jimmy asked me and my mate if we wanted a bath.

The local bath-house was exactly that — a house full of

bath-tubs and showers. You'd think the Corporation would have found it just as economical to instal the tubs in the city dwellers' homes. However, it was just as well they didn't because the bath-house now served a dual purpose as a 'Poison Gas Decontamination Centre'.

'Mustard gas victims to the left!' stated a red and white placard. 'Decontamination centre open day and night. Bath-house closes at 6 p.m.'

Another notice directed us down the long white-tiled corridor, and the familiar smell of chlorine smacked at our young noses.

'What do you want?' enquired an old civil defence volunteer in a steel helmet and black wellington boots.

'We're mustard gas victims,' said Jim.

'Fuck off!' replied the old man. 'Who the fuckin' hell do you think you're talking to? Fuckin' sailors! I've shit better fuckin' sailors than you.'

This was normal Liverpool badinage, and only to be expected. Young people accepted verbal abuse from their elders, and the elders usually won the verbal battle because they knew more foul language.

'Go swallow a fathom of my shite!' parried young Jim.

A blousy-looking woman in a damp red turban saved us from getting deeper into verbal manure by shouting down the corridor: 'This way! Take one, two and three, and pull the bloody plugs out when you've finished, dirty buggers.'

Clithero felt quite insulted.

'Don't worry about it,' said Jimmy. I've been coming to this place all my life and I know the old bag. She says that to everyone. She thinks only dirty buggers wash.'

We left the bath-house feeling clean and bright. Jimmy put his best naval uniform on, and Jackie fished out a freshly laundered pair of scarlet trunks. I pinched them right away. He didn't really mind and helped himself to a new pair of yellow and black running shorts from my kit.

The big do started in the Legs of Man, an alehouse famous throughout Merseyside. It had three huge brass legs hanging from the wall outside and was a recognised meeting-place. 'See you under the Legs of Man' was just as common as 'Meet you under the big clock.' When they ran out of glasses, the management used jam-jars; glasses had no wartime priority and were not being produced. Drinking straight from the bottle would have eased the situation. Unfortunately, even the youngest drinker wanted pints of mixed; bottles were for females and Yanks.

Most of the young generation were away at sea or getting their heads blown off on some crazy battlefield. The women's navy and the women's army took a lot of the girls; consequently, the do consisted of mature people too old for the forces, a few dockland workers — far too important to be used as cannon fodder, other people in reserved occupations and a few guys on leave or home from the sea. You might have thought it would turn into an old-fashioned 'knees up', but this was not so.

'How ya gonna keep 'em down on the farm . . .' Clithero belted out the old song on the piano. 'Jazzin' around! Seein' the town . . .' Sixty or seventy people were jazzin' around the Campello living-room.

Jazzing is a word used all over the world. To the Liverpudlian, it meant dancing, any kind of dancing. 'See you at the jazz' could mean 'I'll meet you at the best restaurant in town and dance with you,' or it could mean 'I'll be at the threepenny hop over Burton's the tailors.' Every Burton's men's wear shop in the country had a ballroom above.

The natives were proud of their skill on the dance floor. No matter how crowded the ballroom, a good dancer would not bump into another couple. If you did have the odd bump, you apologised: 'Sorry, missus! It's me tart's 'igh 'eels.'

The Campello boys could really swing! I was no mean hoofer myself, nor was Clithero. However, he was stuck with the piano and loved it. It was crazy! There was not enough room betewen the couples to insert a postcard, but they danced on a sixpence — spinning, twisting and swinging around without touching. One or two drunks managed to collapse of course, and this gave a little extra space for the big fat mammas and stout uncles. As the night wore on, so the dancers thinned out. Rosie could really go! I danced with her a few times but she was at her best when swinging with young Tony. He'd learned to jitterbug in New York and they caused a sensation with their skilful acrobatic steps. Everyone cheered.

'I'm knocked out!' admitted Tony about 3 a.m. 'This is gonna go on all night long. How about you? Are you ready for bed?'

'I certainly am,' I replied, 'but I feel mean leaving my friend.'

Not a word of our little affair of the previous night had passed our lips. If it hadn't been for the sweet kiss and loving embrace, I'd have thought it all a dream. but it was reality, genuine, and looked like it was going to start all over again.

'You couldn't get him away from that piano with a crowbar,' Tony said in a matter-of-fact voice. 'Look at him. He's having the time of his life. Come and see ma. She's fixing you up in my room.'

The Campello family had known me all my life, though I could hardly have described them as friends — schoolfriends perhaps, or friends of Mrs Jones's family. They were not even neighbours, and indeed lived in a better part of the city, in a comfortable and well-appointed home.

Tony's mother was extremely kind. 'Don't worry about the boy at the piano,' she said, taking my arm. 'I'll make sure he sleeps in a comfortable bed and see that he gets a bite of breakfast when he wakes up.' She led us into her son's room, slid open the wardrobe door, removed my smart blue and gold dress jacket and hung it up for me.

I'd never seen so many clothes in one wardrobe in my life; suits, hats, shirts, dresses, silken gowns and embroidered smoking-jackets. It was like something you see at the movies when the star is deciding which tie he should wear.

Tony wore the first button-down shirt I had ever seen. English shirts only opened to the throat. He peeled the shirt from his firm brown shoulders and his mother pulled back the bed covers. 'You'll be comfortable in here,' she said, taking her son's white shirt. 'Tony will find you something to sleep in, won't you dear?'

'He sleeps in his skin,' Tony said as he slipped out of his smart-looking trousers. His mother patted his sleek black hair and left us.

The room contained a chest of drawers, Tony's single bed, a side table, built-in wardrobe and a modern hand-basin with hot and cold running water. Thick blackout material covered the windows. I looked at it and blurted out, 'Tony! There was no air raid tonight. They won't come at this time. Perhaps it's all over.'

'Ain't even started,' he said through a mouthful of toothpaste. 'They've been going over all night. Some other poor bastards are having a share.'

I hung my trousers up and pulled off the bright satin briefs belonging to Clithero. Tonly looked at the swelling in the elasticated backless support I wore. 'Do you need anything?' he asked.

'My toothbrush,' I answered. 'I left it at Rosie's place.'

'You can use mine,' said the lovely boy. 'I don't mind . . . if you don't.'

I brushed my teeth and could see Tony in the mirror removing his bright polka-dot briefs. Wow! A quick rinse under the tap, a rinse for Tony's toothbrush and I was ready.

We just gazed at each other in admiration. Words seemed inappropriate, unsuitable and quite unnecessary. He wanted to stand before me as he was, showing me his beauty; his dark, long-lashed eyes, his lovely olivine skin, green and gold and shining with the grace of his magnificent Italian ancestry; a true son of the gods of ancient Rome. The long muscular legs and perfect symmetry of his form excited and pleased my senses.

Here stood a real boy. Beautiful as only a sixteen-year-old boy can be: fine rippling stomach muscles, healthy, glowing body and perfect-sized sex, neat trim triangle of silky pubic hair and firm round testicles tight against his superb erect penis, every tiny vein standing out clear blue with the pink unsheathed end moist and shiny beneath the soft glow of the light. Lovers, male and female, must always have stood like this and gazed in admiration before giving their bodies freely, and with pure love . . .

Tony pulled a garment from under his pillow, looked me straight in the eyes, held my gaze for perhaps two seconds and slid into the soft comfortable bed.

'You are beautiful! Beautiful! Beautiful!' I whispered, stroking, petting, caressing and kissing at his warm soft skin.

'Stroke me! Stroke me Jackie,' he whispered, writhing in ecstacy beneath my caresses. The flimsy nylon garment he wore moved against our skin and sent shivers of delight running over us in a stream of sensuous pleasure. 'Stroke me. Keep stroking,' he continued. He simply needed love and I gave him all I had. The final kiss would come later, and I looked forward to the end of the petting when I would enter into his gorgeous body.

Tony reached for the support, hooked his fingers and tore it from me. I knew he was ready and wanted me inside him. Natural lubrication assisted us. A simple penetration as before, holding back, and only giving as much as he desired. The magic fluid would pass into this wonderful young creature smiling up at me. He took my hand and placed it beneath the silky garment. His lovely erection throbbed beneath the muscles of my abdomen. I gave him just a little more penis and Tony trembled beneath me; I knew he must be on the verge of coming.

'Little sweetheart,' I whispered softly. 'Can you take it all?'

'Yes. Give it to me. All of it. Go now!'

A long, slow sensuous drive completed the penetration, testicles hard against his firm round bottom. Fortunately, he managed to hold on until my speedy movements brought a climax and we shot together. Our lips met. We kissed, and my sweet little catch slept in my arms. It was delightful just feeling his heart beat against mine. Eventually I slept and dreamed he was a girl.

The blacked-out windows prevented me from knowing if it was day or night. A hand stroked at my hair.

'Can I switch the lights on?' asked his mother's voice.

'Yes, momma. It's quite alright,' answered the boy. She switched on the light, removed her son's arm from round my neck and touched my forehead with her lips. Tony sat up beside me, his face glowing with health and his hair untidy from sleeping. Momma placed a huge breakfast tray on the side table, and kissed her boy's smooth cheek.

'Are you happy now, darling?' she asked.

I put my arm around the lovely girl-boy and squeezed him to me.

'Very happy,' he said softly. 'Please ask Jackie to stay again tonight.'

She rumpled my short curly hair, picked up the discarded jock strap from the carpet and said quietly, 'He'll stay.'

She closed the door behind her and the Yale lock clicked. I knew now why it had been installed.

'Will you stay tonight?' asked Tony Campello. 'You and momma are the only two people in the world who know.'

He sank his pearly white teeth into a crisp piece of buttered toast and smiled at me with his lovely eyes.

'I'd love to stay, sweetheart,' I replied. 'I'm not being wicked when I call you sweetheart, am I? It just comes natural.'

He licked at his strong white teeth, rubbed against me like a silky little kitten and almost made me spill my coffee.

Most of the guests had gone home, so we had the freedom of the house and were able to make use of the bathroom and shower. We returned to Tony's room wrapped in cotton towelling gowns. His mother had laid out two pairs of silky girl's knickers, while two flimsy little nighties were folded on the pillows.

With no show of embarrassment whatever, Tony stepped into a pair of knickers and pulled them up around his little bottom. 'How about you?' he asked, holding out a pair of lace-trimmed panties.

'Not for me, Tony. I'll wear my jock strap and trunks, if that's okay with you.'

He giggled and continued to dress.

Jackie Clithero played a good game of snooker. Most of the decent-sized pubs in Liverpool had a billiards room and snooker was very popular. Tony, being a seafarer, didn't get as much practice as Clithero and I. Even on a ship like the *Queen Mary*, snooker was impossible.

Clithero teamed up with Jimmy Jones just to make things reasonably even, and we played four-handed snooker. 'What's happening tonight?' enquired Clithero as he scattered the reds.

'Fuck all!' replied Jimmy, chalking his cue. 'Me mam will get a few beers in I suppose. Will you knock out a tune on the old joanna?'

'Try and stop him,' said I and potted a red.

An old grey-haired guy stood in as marker and slid the polished mahogany brass-tipped pointer to number one. I potted the pink and the old geezer moved the pointer to number seven. Someone else called, 'Hey, fetch us a round of drinks, dad,' and the old guy buggered off. I missed the next shot. Jimmy potted a red and said, 'What's the stakes?'

'I don't gamble,' Tony said over the table. His lovely youthful body fascinated me. I wanted to help him with his shot, lean across him and press my stiffened penis against his gorgeous firm bottom.

Jackie saw the hungry look in my eye. 'Did you sleep with young Tony last night?' he asked as we fiddled with the marker board.

No power on earth would have got me to discuss Tony and his little private ways. In fact I felt as if something dreadful would happen to me if I did. 'I slept in his room, and I've been invited to spend the night again,' I admitted. 'Do you mind?'

'It's okay,' replied my friend. Don't worry about me. I'm having the time of my life. I never knew such wonderful people existed.'

'Come on, Jackie! We're fuckin' twelve behind,' called Jim. 'Losers pay for the friggin' ale! Even if they don't fuckin' gamble,' he added, poking Tony in the ribs with a cue.

'Back off, stranger,' Tony said in a perfect impersonation of Gary Cooper. 'This town ain't big enough for the two of us.'

The evening went well and I walked Tony home after the all clear sounded. His mother was expecting us. Tony's bedroom looked extra bright — fresh flowers on the side table and a flimsy nightie on each pillow. She watched her son strip down to his girl's panties and slip on a nightie as I washed at the hand-basin.

The boy slid into bed. I slipped off my scarlet trunks, hesitated for a moment, saw the expectant look in her eye and thought 'What the hell!' She held back the covers for me and I pulled the support from my stiffened penis. 'Good night,' she said as I got into bed with a big hard-on. Tony was in my arms before she went out of the door.

The ten days' leave passed all too quickly and we had to return to our camp at Chester. However, Tony's ship would dock every few weeks so I knew we'd be able to see each other from time to time. I couldn't settle down after that. I needed a beautiful young boy and became far too masculine for Clithero who wanted a soft feminine companion.

Jamie showed up out of the blue. He'd been in Greece, Crete, Egypt, everywhere. He was stationed on the racecourse at Chester, and slept in a stable. Naturally, I visited him many times, told him I loved him madly and always would. However, he still resisted me.

Clithero wanted me, I wanted Jamie, and Jamie didn't know what the hell he wanted. It was too much for me. I was almost twenty, and life was calling . . .

A major and a sergeant called at our camp asking for volunteers for a strange new unit. When I was interviewed I liked them instantly because the major called me by my first name and lit my cigarette for me, something beyond my wildest dreams. The sergeant used the foulest language in front of the officer, again something absolutely unimaginable.

They asked a few simple questions, even though they had my regimental history in front of them and probably knew more about me than I did myself.

'Why volunteer?' the major asked.

'To be quite honest,' I said. 'I'm fucked if I know!'

'Next!' called the sergeant . . .

Clithero and Jamie met me in a downtown pub a few days later. 'The drinks are on me,' I said foolishly. 'I'm leaving you guys.'

'Don't tell me you volunteered for that stupid fuckin' SS thing,' said Jamie.

'Yeah!' I replied casually. 'I've been accepted. I'm off to bonny Scotland where the boys wear skirts. I leave for Fort William at the end of the week.'

I knew I wasn't tough and I knew I wasn't brave. I realised that I was not really a masculine young man but I wanted to find out the truth; test myself and hope that other people would regard me as a man.

We fell into a huddle the night before my departure, three frightened homosexual boys. 'Look after each other,' I begged them. 'There's no turning back for me.'

5. Here's to the Dead Already!

Unfortunately I had to hand in my hard-earned stripes. It was understood by all concerned that the NCOs would have to start from scratch, earn promotion in the new unit and integrate with guys from every regiment in the British forces.

Duffy met me coming from the CO's office. 'Did you do it?' he enquired.

'Yeah. I'm off to Scotland at the end of the week. Fuck this lot. I'll be training recruits till the war ends.'

'I'm with you,' said Duffy. He walked into the office and joined the new commando with me.

Duffy and I reached Fort William and made our way to the foot of Ben Nevis. But when we saw the training camp, we wondered what we'd let ourselves in for. There was nothing there, just a few wooden huts. Guys from every regiment in the army sat around in the grass, wicked fighting knives strapped to the calf. They were strange-looking troops, lean and hungry with bored faces, guys who knew it all, overtrained and chomping at the bit. Most of them had been NCOs, judging by the marks on their tunics where corporals' stripes and sergeants' chevrons had been.

A hard-faced Liverpudlian approached me. 'Are you from Liverpool?' he enquired.

'Yeah! This is my mate Duffy. He's from the Pool too.'

Another guy joined us — a real broken-nosed pug, overweight with a beer-drinker's belly, dopey face, Dublin accent, badly dressed and sloppy looking.

'This is Spike McCormack,' said the Liverpool guy. 'My name's Gordon Beattie. Spike's the middleweight champion of Ireland. He fought for the Golden Gloves in the States.'

'Never heard of him!' said Duffy.

'And I never heard of you,' replied Spike. 'The nearest boozer is five miles away. Let's piss off and get a few jars down us.'

There was no discipline, no parades, nothing — just a bunch of officers and men. The army catering corps fed the troops in a makeshift canteen. The food was good and there was plenty of it, but some of the lads hunted deer and sheep in Nevis forest. They butchered the carcasses and nailed the heads to the chalet doors.

Each man wore the cap badge of his parent unit. Small groups were formed and numbered. Hand-written notices appeared on the camp notice-board and gave the daily routine: a constant barrage of instruction. Specialist sergeants gave lessons in various skills: high explosives, demolition, knife fighting, unarmed combat and map reading. We drove foreign vehicles and railway locomotives and handled strange weapons, becoming familiar with ammunition and detonators unknown to British troops.

Spike McCormack and his Liverpool friend Gordon Beattie teamed up with me and Duffy, forming a close companionship. We trained side by side and clung together when things got tough. It was a strange mob: there were actors, poets and artists. Villians and roughnecks and simple guys like myself rubbed shoulders with intellectuals, linguists and men with university degrees. Some guys wore foreign decorations, ribbons they'd earned in the armies of the world.

As the days wore on, friendships developed. Small groups of men teamed up, depended on their close companions and helped each other in hard times — endurance tests, route marches, rock climbing and mountain walking. Amazingly fit and self-reliant, the small teams slowly tightened up into one exciting SS unit. When the commander was satisfied with our progress, he packed us off to Fort William and handed us over to the navy. They dubbed us the Special Boat Service, send us out to sea and tried to drown us.

As time went by, a great spirit of comradeship sprang up between the SS and the navy guys. They taught us many skills, a new nautical language, and shared the daily rum ration, getting drunk as skunks — the one thing that everyone had in common. The War Office described us as Commando battalions, and the German high command called us redskins and savages.

Duffy was the first to go. He copped three stripes and moved out to a secret air base to train as a sergeant glider pilot. I didn't fancy flying a glider, so we said goodbye and parted company.

Spike and Gordon stuck with me until I moved into a secret army called the SAS. Now I went to Manchester and became a lodger with a civilian family in Wythenshawe who had a comfortable home near Ringway aerodrome, the parachute training school of the SAS. Things brightened up. I got drunk every night, had a sweet fellow lodger and a little extra pay in my pocket.

A team of RAF guys put us through some initial training in a harness — no parachute, just a makeshift trapeze and a landing mat in a hangar. Then some Polish freedom fighters gave a demonstration jump at Tatton Park, leaping from a low-flying aircraft to hit the deck in ten seconds. It looked easy enough, so I approached my first jump with reasonable confidence. A medium-sized barrage balloon took us aloft in groups of four, then we jumped off one by one. It was quite simple but the parachute was old-fashioned and bulky — a great yellow canopy with a two-foot hole in the roof and a little thing called a pilot chute. A jump from a low-flying aircraft at 200 feet meant that the parachute was still swinging when you touched down. A few guys were injured and one or two even got killed.

As we had no official status and no parade ground, we left our private homes each night and met in a pub called the George. Someone stole a song from the Royal Flying Corps of the previous war, jazzed it up and named it the song of the SAS: 'Stand by your glasses ready, here's to the man in the sky. Three cheers for the dead already, and here's to the next man to die.' When some unfortunate bastard got killed, we sang him out at the George and smashed the glasses in the fireplace!

A few minor injuries came my way; a runaway chute dragged me through the mud, face down, eyes full of stones and grit. Someone washed the chippings from my eyes, and when the sight returned a couple of days later I was in the air again. Then a smashed knee put me out of action for a week, so I borrowed a walking-stick and called at Jamie Dunlop's home a few miles away. Unfortunately, he wasn't there.

I'd earned my wings by this time, a tiny silver and blue enamel affair, worn in the scarlet trim of a forage cap. The regular parachute wings at my shoulder, a fighting knife at the calf, strange jumping boots and an SAS smock formed the trappings of my unit — a rag-tag uniform unknown and unseen by the public as yet. The whole affair seemed quite romantic, exciting, wonderful . . .

Jamie's mother wasn't impressed. 'Oh dear!' she said. 'What's happened? What's the walking-stick for? Have you broken any bones?'

Timmy came home from work and made a fuss. The silly trappings of war fascinated the boy. He had a thousand questions to ask, and I enjoyed discussing the things that went on at Ringway. We were deep in conversation when Jamie rang and I answered the phone.

'Can't get away,' he said. 'I'm on duty. Why don't you come to Chester? We have an all-ranks dance every weekend, and you could meet all your old mates and enjoy yourself.'

'Another time,' I said, explaining the injured knee.

'Well, come when it's better,' replied Jamie. 'I'm dying to see you.'

'So long, kid. I'll drop in and see you when I get time. Here's your mum.'

It was twelve o'clock when the front door opened and Jamie's old man walked in, silver and matt-black stud in his dress shirt, thinning hair brushed back, shiny with brylcreem, neat bow tie, hand-tied and dinky, shoes gleaming, trousers sharp as a razor.

'Well!' he exclaimed as he slipped off his dinner-jacket. 'Look what the wind's blown in! How are you, lad?'

His wife kissed him on the cheek, I said I was fine and she made some cocoa.

They went upstairs about ten minutes later, Timmy and I following shortly afterwards. He went into the bathroom and I got ready for bed. Timmy took his time, splashed about and made a hell of a noise. He returned bare-chested, pink-faced and fragrant, pyjama trousers clinging to his long damp legs.

'You look different,' he said as he jumped in beside me. 'You've changed. All grown up and mature.'

'I'm twenty years old!'

'You were only eighteen last time we slept in this bed.'

'And you were only sixteen. I thought you might have forgotten about it.'

'Have you?' he asked, sweet-smelling breath in my nostrils.

'I haven't changed that much. Jesus! You're a lovely kid.'

His fingers crept up my shorts, soft fair hair across my eyes, lips at my face.

'You don't shave,' he whispered.

'Not yet.'

'I shave every week.'

'You're more masculine than me, Timmy. Kiss me again.'

He felt my bare bottom in the most exciting exploration, kissed my breast, pulled off my knickers and gave me his youthful body. I watched his lovely eyes light up, felt him stiffen inside me, shared the love he offered. He made love silently, held me firm, gave all he had and kept it moving till the end, grunting with satisfaction when the exciting moment came and slippy love seeds escaped like shooting stars. A little kissing came my way as we held hands and relaxed in the feather-bed.

'Do you want to come?' he asked, parted lips awaiting me, young mouth hovering over my pubic region.

'It's okay, Timmy. You don't have to do that.'

'I do,' he said slowly. 'I really do!'

Kissing his sweet lips came naturally and so did the taste of the love we shared.

Back in Ringway once again, fighting fit and fit for fighting, I managed a few night jumps, leapt from a plane in the darkened sky and felt the hand of God. He came to me in my loneliness, held me over Tatton Park and put me down like a feather.

The unit moved to Congleton and I moved into a luxurious house called the Vicarage. What splendour! Unfortunately I made a simple mistake on the first night, walked into the wrong bedroom and found myself with a housemaid named Jane, a pretty little thing, sweet seventeen and never been kissed. Jane was startled and I was naked.

'Don't go!' she said as I made for the door. 'Someone will hear you.'

I grabbed a gown and covered myself. The floorboards squeaked on the outside landing. Jane put a finger to her lips. Someone pulled a lavatory chain, moved along the creaky corridor and banged a door.

'That'll be the butler,' Jane said. 'He always goes about at this time.'

I made a move.

'Wait a few minutes,' she asked. 'If the missus finds out she'll kill me.'

'Give me something to wear', I asked. 'I feel foolish like this.'

Jane laughed and threw me a pair of her knickers. 'I've never seen a naked boy before,' she said delightfully.

'I've never seen a naked girl,' I replied.

She sat up in bed, a lovely lass with pointed breasts and soft brown hair.

'You're excited,' she said. 'Please, let me look!'

'No.'

'Please?'

'Just a peep, then I must go.'

She gasped with pleasure and surprise. 'Can I touch it?'

'No!' I said, pulled the flimsy knickers up and ran from the room.

We became quite friendly as the days passed. She soon discovered my lack of interest in the opposite sex, and the friendship developed into a brother and sister affair.

Most of the guys spent the days in local cafes, drank coffee by the gallon, ate dainty pastries by the dozen and boozed away the nights in local pubs. Once again, our HQ and recognised parade ground was an alehouse.

Bill Leonard came into my life at Congleton, a sergeant instructor, worshipped by his colleagues and admired by all concerned. He was an expert at all things, a champion boxer, wonderful athlete, spell-binding lecturer and amazing soldier.

Decorations for bravery, campaign ribbons on his chest, Bill could have been twenty-eight or thirty years of age, but older guys like Bill didn't interest me. Consequently, when he took me under his wing and became my friend, I felt quite flattered and saw no sexual content in the relationship. Superman! I wondered what he saw in me.

We lived quite dangerously, I suppose. Anything was liable to happen: visits to enemy territory, midnight landings and secret operations took place from time to time. You had to be alert, aware of unfamiliar explosives, new weapons and bombs at our disposal. Detonating propelling pens were part of our everyday equipment. New ideas and all kinds of crazy experiments were carried out by the SAS and Bill Leonard was one of the kingpins in the unit. So I treasured his friendship and learned as much as possible from the man.

The boys gathered round one Saturday morning and listened to a lecture on the Thompson submachine-gun. 'This is the weapon for close quarters,' said Bill. 'The old gangsters of the twenties proved it again and again, so get acquainted with the bloody thing.'

There were many close-quarter weapons, but if Bill said the Tommy gun was the best, then that was that.

The men filed off at the end of the session, and I stayed to help pack the equipment away.

'Where are you going for the weekend?' asked Bill.

'Going to see my mate in Chester,' I replied. 'There's an all-ranks dance at the Dale, so there should be plenty of crumpet about.'

'I'm coming with you,' he said, which meant he was coming with me.

Jamie and Jackie Clithero were there. They hadn't seen the SAS in uniform, so naturally enough they had a lot of questions to ask.

'You look like a fuckin' pirate!' said Clithero. 'What kinda uniform is that?'

'Balls!' I replied. 'We don't have a regular outfit. The officers are cushy and no one cares how we dress. But there is talk of new designs — red berets for Airborne, green for Commando and a stone-coloured hat for the SAS.

'Red hat and no drawers!' Clithero said. 'I think I'll volunteer.'

'What's it like when you go out of a plane?' asked Jamie.

'Easy! Just like fallin' offa fuckin' skyscraper.'

Bill Leonard came on the scene so I introduced him to the lads. He danced with every girl in the place, took over the microphone, sang all the pop songs, acted as master of ceremonies and dished out the prizes for the spotlight waltz.

'He's a fuckin' dynamo!' Clithero observed. 'Is he one of your crew?'

'Bill? He's the boss!'

'Looks like a hard bastard!'

Bill crooned the last waltz over the microphone: 'Who's taking you home tonight, after the dance is through? Who's the lucky boy . . . going your way . . .?'

The ballroom rang with applause and stomping feet. 'More! More!' shouted the crowd.

Bill Leonard raised his hand and shut them up. 'That's it!' he said firmly. 'It's all over, kids!'

The regimental police came on the scene and escorted the visitors to the gates. Jamie and Clithero said goodbye to me. I wanted to stay but it wasn't possible, so I went off with Bill.

'Where are you staying?' he asked.

'Home. Congleton. There's a regular train service.'

'Don't be like that!' Bill said. 'What's wrong with you? It's Sunday tomorrow and there's nothing in Congleton. Let's stay in a hotel. We can get a few more drinks from the night porter.'

In the lounge he put his hand on my knee. 'I'd love to fuck you!' he said. 'I get the horn just looking at you. You're a peach!'

'Jesus! What are you saying? Come on. You've had too much to drink.'

'I mean it,' said Bill. 'You don't fool me. I'm staying and you're staying with me.'

I didn't really like older guys, so I said, 'Why don't you find a girl?'

Bill took my hand and stroked the back of my wrist. 'I think I've found one,' he said. 'Don't you?'

'Please, Bill. You'll get us thrown out!'

'I like you,' he said softly. 'I've been chasing after you for weeks and you know it. You've hardly left my side. Those big eyelashes of yours . . . the way you look at me. You must feel something. That Clithero guy almost kissed you when the dance finished. How do you think I felt? The great Bill Leonard is only human. You're a nice friendly boy, Jack, and I want to love you. I'm not just after your ring. There's more to it than that. You're lovely!'

'You're just confusing me, Bill. I haven't been with a man. Not really. Clithero was my boyfriend before I came into this mob.'

'I've been in love with you for months, sweet face. You're the perfect boy for me. I like a military kid and you're just waiting to be kissed, aren't you.'

The magic got to work and drew us close. Hands clasped and fingers squeezed.

'Please let me take you to bed,' he said quietly. 'I do love you.'

'Okay, Bill.'

The bedroom door was still open when he took me in his arms and closed it with the heel of his boot.

'Mmmm! Bill . . .'

His chin was bristly but his lips were soft and gentle. His hand stroked my bare bottom, made me excited; I lifted my arms and put them round his neck. He raised the tail of my shirt, kissed my bottom and said, for some unknown reason, 'Keep your socks on, kid.'

Bill could do anything! And he did it better than the next guy.

There was talk of a move to Chesterfield, the new home of the Airborne forces. None of my mates had seen them as yet but we'd made a few experimental drops for them, tested out the newly designed helmets they were to use and heard of the parachute battalions and glider pilot mobs. Unfortunately, we still wore the canvas and sponge helmet, jumped in shirtsleeves and got knocked about a bit. The French guys jumped in soft shoes and civilian clothes, and the Polish freedom mob were so tough it was said that they didn't need a parachute at all.

Meanwhile, a few more accidents came my way. A badly fitted harness injured one of my testicles. A nurse at Manchester Royal Infirmary pulled my shorts down and my shirt up, so I grabbed my shirt and pulled it down again.

'What's the matter with you?'

'I'm shy,' said I, blushing like a girl.

The doctor pulled it up again and took my testicle in his cold hand. 'It's a bit bruised,' he said, squeezing the swollen ball in his fingers, 'but we can soon fix that!'

The nurse came at me with a hypodermic as big as a bicycle pump, so I grabbed my shirt, she grabbed my balls and shoved the needle in as far as it would go. The female hands scared me more than the syringe.

'Take it easy, you daft bitch!'

She showed her teeth, pulled back the plunger and filled the phial with honey-coloured fluid from my knackers.

'Take a couple of days off duty,' the doctor said as the swollen goolie returned to its normal size. 'What do you do, by the way?'

'I jump out of airplanes.'

'That's not a very sensible occupation,' he replied. 'You're going to hurt yourself. Better take a week off.'

I rather liked him after that. So I pulled up my pants, gave the nurse a nasty look and pissed off as quick as I could.

The coalfields of Lancashire were not far away, so I grabbed a train, called at Jamie's and found him home on leave.

The old man came in from the hotel and went through his Saturday night ritual. He said, 'Hey, hey! The gang's all here,' slipped off his dinner-jacket, kissed his wife, drank his cocoa and disappeared off to bed.

'You look absolutely fantastic!' Jamie said in the bedroom, a statement which, naturally enough, sent the blood rushing to all the right places and made me kiss the lovely boy on the nose. 'I've been accepted by the Airborne forces,' he said as he jumped into bed.'

'Perhaps we'll finish up in the same mob,' I replied and cuddled into the gorgeous boy.

He snuggled down, took my kisses on his mouth, felt my lips at his breast and gripped me in his hands. Exchanging kisses thrilled me. We rolled about, Jamie on top, underneath and back again, an exciting tussle, springy erections hot and horny, bursting with love.

He stretched out flat, clutched the sides of the mattress. 'You've wanted to do it for a long time,' he said. 'Now do it!'

The boy's shoulders and legs were golden brown, delicious, smooth as silk and breathtakingly beautiful. His bottom was white, clear-skinned and firm with youthful muscle. He showed me exactly where to go, made it perfectly clear and waited for my journey to commence. Too late! All my love escaped in the excitement. Jamie felt its warm flow, held me close, kissed me and spilled his sweetness on my naked chest.

'That's it!' he said. 'It's always the same. We might as well forget about it.'

'It was beautiful!' I argued. 'What's wrong? We can try again. You just made me too excited. I love you. Just thinking about you makes me come.'

'No more!' he said seriously. 'We've been trying for three years. It's not good. I need someone, a guy who makes me happy. We're like two wives without a husband. You must know how I feel, Jackie boy. You're like me! You need a man.'

'But I love you. I want you, Jamie. I'm different with you.'

'You're not,' he said. 'Sweetheart, you are just like a girl. I love you and I always will, but I need a guy. Try and understand.'

My boyfriends had given plenty of love and affection. I hadn't even thought about it. Love was always there and couldn't be turned on and off, no matter what the problem.

Jamie looked a treat when he got out of bed and moved into the bathroom. It was a bit too much for me, so I left after breakfast, took the train to Liverpool and called at Annie Jones' home in the

Buildings.

Things changed after that. I don't think I became more feminine but I put Jamie out of my mind and spent the nights in Bill Leonard's arms. He loved me and his tender words of endearment made me happy.

The unit duly moved to Chesterfield, the town of the crooked spire. The camp was a place called Ardwick, the new Airborne HQ. My rag-tag mob had to settle in, accept the camp discipline and a different way of life altogether. The comfortable billets we'd become used to were lost and gone forever.

Most of the parachute drops had been from the deck of a Whitley bomber. At Chesterfield we used Manchesters and Lancasters. Not too much difference but just enough for another accident. I came out of a flying kite, landed hard on my own hand-grenade and smashed a couple of ribs. The quack strapped me up, breathing became difficult and a few nights later I woke up screaming with pain.

Lancaster . . . Manchester . . . it all seemed so strange. I dreamed about the two important towns in my life and found myself in a Lancaster sanatorium. It was my twenty-first birthday and there was a greetings telegram on the side table: 'Happy landings! Your fair admirers.' I never discovered where it came from or who sent it, but kept the stupid thing for years.

'You're going home,' said the doctor. 'Take it easy and you should live a few more years, but don't overdo it.'

'What's wrong with me?'

'TB. Don't get upset. Plenty of fresh air and good food will work wonders. You'll get a life pension from the army, so things won't be as bad as you think.'

There was no cure for the dreadful disease. No one wrote or contacted me, but I didn't mind as I felt like a leper, a contagious carrier of some frightening plague.

The weeks passed slowly. The room was a three-walled affair, a private isolation cell with an open front and no doors. The moon shone through my open room and shed a little silver on the polished floor. The night nurse called to see me, stroked my hair and tried to raise a smile.

'Don't be so glum,' she said. 'What's wrong?'

'I miss my boyfriend.'

'That's good,' she said. 'A few jokes like that and you'll be up and about in no time.'

'I'm not joking,' I said deliberately. 'I've got a boyfriend. Girls don't interest me at all.'

She was a pretty little thing, an Irish girl with soft black curls and a lovely face.

'Don't kiss me!' I said as her lips came close. 'You'll catch tuberculosis.'

She kissed me, took off her knickers and hung them on a screen.

'Please don't!'

The Irish girl slipped into my bed and kissed my lips again. 'You're not infectious,' she said, 'and you never will be. It's cleared up. There's a little scar tissue on one lung. That's all. Do you believe me now?'

She didn't quite convince me but we made love and I had my first girl, the most unnatural act I had ever performed in my life.

Still in the rag-tag uniform of the SAS, I left the hospital and went in search of my mother and sister. They'd been split up and evacuated after the house had been blown up. The Red Cross put me in touch with my sister who was in South Wales. Mother was with a family in Lancaster. Here we go again . . .

I rented a house in Liverpool for thirty shillings a week, put a few sticks of furniture in the joint and shot across to Wales. Sis was pleased to see me, but I couldn't let her kiss my lips and was too ashamed to mention the terrible disease. Mother came next. I dragged her back to Liverpool and settled her in the new home with my sister. A few days later, the army pension came through and a month's leave pending discharge.

'That's it!' I thought. 'I'm going to get fit or kill myself trying. I ain't gonna be a pensioner!'

Jamie still bothered me. I loved him madly, had to see him and wondered how to break the news. A telephone call put me in touch. He was home and waiting for me, sergeant's stripes on his arm, the red beret of the Paratroops on his handsome head and a smile on his lovely face.

'I missed you,' he said in my arms. 'Why didn't you keep in touch?'

'It's all over, Jamie. I'm going to buy a civilian suit and work for my living. I've been discharged.'

We cried in his bed. Never again would I kiss his sweet red lips but we made love and he was satisfied at last.

Before we parted, Jamie gave me a forty-five automatic and a few rounds of ammunition — private possessions that he wanted to exchange for my fighting knife, a beautiful weapon, perfectly balanced, made and designed by the Wilkinson Sword Company. He'd always admired the gleaming blade of death and couldn't buy one anywhere.

So, with Jamie's forty-five in my kick, I returned to Liverpool and went into training, weight-lifting, swimming, and running for miles.

6. First Tripper

The morning sun came out to greet me, so I said hello and hit the dockland streets. It was wonderful! A whole new world existed and I hadn't even noticed. A new exciting world, a world of plenty, thousands of jobs, plenty of money, hundreds of empty houses and countless vacant flats.

Jobs! Jobs! Jobs! Engineers wanted! No experience required! Train as you go! Double pay for night shift! Men wanted! Women wanted! Houses and flats to rent!

The streets were alive with handsome men and lovely boys from every place on earth — sparkling young Americans, snazzy guys from France, wonderful kids from Canada, New Zealand and Australia, tough troops from Poland, laughing Dutch lads and men from Czechoslovakia. A great cavalcade of sparkling youth, an Easter parade on the city pavements. The whole wide world was on the move and it seemed to start in Liverpool.

The Shipping Federation fascinated me — a dirty place, bare boards and crushed cigarette packets underfoot, dusty windows and draughty corridors, not unlike a job centre but exactly like the dole. The walls were lined with colourful seafarers, Yanks and Poles and grinning Lascars, ship's boys and carpenters, Chinese and Singalese and men from sunny Singapore and Spain. A family of salt-water men home from the sea.

Deckhands wanted! Able-bodied seamen apply here! Cunarders signing on!

My lips smacked. The sound of the sea came roaring in my ears. I heard the ocean rollers, smelt the salty wash and asked a guy at a desk for a job.

'Last ship?' he asked.

'First tripper,' I replied, 'but I've had some experience with small boats.'

'Go across to Birkenhead,' said the clerk. 'See the shore skipper at Alfred Holt's. He's taking men on the China boats.'

'The China boats?'

'The Blue Funnel line. They're running out of Chinese crews.'

With a letter of introduction in my sweaty palm, I shot across the water and met a boy named Jimmy Mack. He was only a kid, a seafaring lad of eighteen, handsome and sparkling, a witty boy with a wonderful vocabulary of foul language and a crop of dark brown curls. Jimmy had sailed the seas since the day he left school, been torpedoed, bombed, shipwrecked and starved in open life-boats.

'Keep off the cargo boats,' he said. 'They're fulla fucken' bugs an' Singapore Joeys, friggin' great cockroaches big as your bollocks! It's the big ships for me. With a bit of luck we should sign on the *Antenor*. She's a trooper, an armed merchant cruiser sailing out of Glasgow. I been with the Blue Funnel every trip and always wanted the *Antenor*.'

The shore skipper sent me back to Canning Place, the home of the Liverpool seaman and centre of the shipping pool. Jimmy took me under his wing, helped me with my papers — passport to the world — and seaman's identity card. The dockside boozers beck-oned us, called us to the bar and filled us up with foaming Guinness.

'You've made a good fucken' start,' said Jimmy Mack. 'Let's get back to Birkenhead before the friggin' office shuts. I don't wanna miss the *Antenor*.'

Fortunately, she wasn't due to sail for a couple of days. The Blue Funnel line signed us on. The office manager gave us an advance of pay and we rolled back to Liverpool with our pockets full of tin. The big test came in the doctor's surgery. He looked at my teeth, squeezed my testicles and said, 'You'll do.'

There she was! The *Antenor*, a lovely vessel, all battleship grey, snow-white decks and bright blue funnel, small guns port and starboard and giant artillery piece poking from the after poop deck. Where are you taking me, my pretty maid?

Her enormous size and great dimensions cast a shadow that blacked out the wharf, but she was sleek and trim and very beautiful. A well deck forward and beneath her pointed prow, a well deck aft and beneath her armoured poop, she looked a picture, just like the ocean-going liners of my dreams. Neat cabin doors, shiny brass knobs and sparkling glass, hundreds of portholes all in a row. A deck and B deck and C deck and D deck . . .

Lifeboats long and sturdy, English oak and polished teak, hung out from the dark grey davits and made me feel secure. Emergency rafts lined the upper deck, huge steel tanks set in slides and tied fast with a single rope. They looked capable of housing a dozen men. A shiny axe stood sharp and lonely beside each raft. One swing with the polished blade would sever the rope and send the life-saving equipment shooting down the slide. Knotted ropes hung from the davits. Scrambling nets, huge rope and ladder and bulky mesh, were rolled and tied to the rails. Radio masts sprouted from the topmost deck, and steel-railed gangways reached out to the quayside.

Blue-trousered and white-shirted stewards passed to and fro, escorting passengers, carrying luggage, giving advice and passing the time of day. Mountains of military equipment lined the dockside. Army officers stood around in groups, and flat-capped stevedores manned the rusty derricks.

'Looks like a trip to India,' said Jimmy.

'What makes you think that?' I asked casually.

'Sun helmets,' replied the boy. 'Where else they gonna wear them? Fucken' Russia?'

The troops came aboard the next morning and spent all day marching up the gangways. By this time I was settled in the glory hole, the quarters of the stewards and catering staff. My shipmate Jim had signed on as able-bodied seaman and was housed in the seamen's accommodation, a cluster of cabins beneath the after poop, known as the fo'c'sle.

I liked young Jim, a real genuine kid from an enormous seafaring clan and a live wire full of wit and humour. We hardly knew each other before he'd introduced me to dozens of young people, cousins, brothers, sisters and other members of his enormous family. He could drink like a fish, never seemed to get drunk and didn't want to chase the girls. That's as much as I knew about him. I supposed we'd get better acquainted as the voyage progressed.

My position as assistant cook put me under the direct supervision of the second chef named Alf, a real character who'd sailed on the world's finest ships and must have felt quite at home in the great kitchens of the lovely vessel beneath our feet.

The troops lived, ate, slept and passed away their time on the mess decks, large timber-decked rooms with bare wooden tables, long bench seats and hooks on the bulkhead walls for the hammocks in which they slept. Special galleys known as troop kitchens were allotted to them and a team known as troop cooks did the catering.

Fortunately, I spent my time in the first-class galley and catered for the wealthy passengers and military big shots. Alf took me under his wing and I became his shadow. The secrets of high-class cuisine poured from his lips and I tried to absorb as much as possible.

The *Antenor* had a special date to keep, so she slipped out on the midnight tide to meet her friends. Out of Glasgow, round the

Kempock point, Gourock bay and into the Firth of Clyde.

There they were! All the beauties of the oceans at anchor in the stream. What a mighty convoy! The *Reina del Pacifico*, the *Strathclyde*, the *Maloja* and the *Multan*, the *Ile de France*, the *Empress of Scotland*, the *Empress of Australia*: graceful, beautiful, colourful queens of the sea, great ocean-going liners packed with troops from everywhere on earth. More than a hundred vessels awaited the sleek *Antenor*.

Some were not so trim and gorgeous: cargo boats from Elder Dempster, old ocean-going tubs from the Bibby line, the Harrison line and every shipping company I'd ever heard of. Meat boats from the Argentine, the Red Star line and the Blue Star line and all the colourful lines in the world. They danced and twinkled on the horizon, held their heads high and tried to look their very best in this magnificent company of ballerinas.

Now silver-grey corvettes, a couple of destroyers and a few frigates came on the scene: the Royal Navy in control with submarine chasers, mine detectors, blue-clad matelots at the rails, the white ensign at the taffrail. Flags of all nations flew: Greek and Dutch, French and Russian, the red ensign and the stars and stripes of Uncle Sam, all clustered together and seeking safety in numbers. Unfortunately, some of them could only make eight knots. Eight miles an hour on a voyage halfway round the world!

Out into the North Atlantic sailed the lovely ladies, small craft peeping out from behind their pretty skirts. Eight miles an hour to the rock of Gibraltar and not a casualty. Who would be the first to take a tin fish in her belly? Who would sink and who would swim and what of the survivors?

Panic struck in the night: the crunch of underwater explosive, the hustle and bustle of speedy corvettes, fast grey frigates. Sirens screamed, depth charges shot into the darkened sky, looped a crazy loop and vanished into the dark green waters of Gibraltar harbour.

Rumours flew thick and fast. Submarines had penetrated the defences. The Royal Navy guys were testing a new type of explosive. Germans and Italians had broken from a prison ship, escaped onto the Spanish mainland ... No one knew the truth until the following morning when the sunken vessels told their own tale. Italian frogmen had been at work on the ocean bed. Frogmen, something new and formidable, another thorn in our salty sides.

With oil and water in the tanks, fresh fruit and vegetables in the cooling lockers, the convoy said goodbye to Gibraltar and left our stricken sisters down below. Ten little Indians ... who was next? Nobody seemed to care. The troops were far too busy being seasick, the catering staff were usually involved in a pig-and-whistle booze-up and the rest of the crew were hardened seafarers who'd seen it all before.

The heat became unbearable during the day, while at night a couple of vessels would vanish. Somebody was picking us off one by one, a sharpshooter from the ocean depths. Freetown, Lagos, Takoradi and Sekondi, a bump in the night and another one copped a torpedo. It was quite disturbing at times but not as frightening as what went on in the glory hole.

It shocked me! Guys called each other names and used words I'd never heard in my life. What was a queer? How could they use such words, call each other fruits and bitches, paint their vacant faces, dye their flowing locks and mince around with hand on hip? Disgusted, I bowed my head in shame, kept well clear of the frightening creatures and lost myself in the never-ending kitchen operations.

Fortunately, this behaviour was confined to the stewards' quarters. Then one of my mates came after me. 'You're a nice boy,' he said. 'Would you like to move into my cabin? I'm by myself and there's a spare bunk.'

'Fuck off,' I replied. 'Fuck off! I'll put you over the side and drown you, you bastard! Do you take me for a fucken' queer?'

I had to get as far from the situation as possible, so I moved into the seamen's quarters with Jimmy and his mates. It wasn't quite as luxurious as the comfortable mid-ship accommodation but the guys were real human beings. Six of us shared a cabin: three sets of double bunks with Jimmy and Lal on the port side, Eddie and Sam on the after bulkhead, me and Franco starboard, a deal table midships, a pisshole and shower on deck.

Porpoise and flying fish joined the slow-moving convoy, swam alongside all through the day and filled the South Atlantic with silvery beauty. They weren't alone, unfortunately. A much more deadly creature joined us in the night, popping up from the salty depths and blasting a floating palace from the horizon. Frigates and corvettes shot away. Sirens screamed. Destroyers gave chase and flames seared the night sky.

'Fuck this,' Franco said. 'I'm sleeping on deck. Who's coming with me?'

Franco was a healthy young teenager, husky like a bear. Patches of skin flapped and hung from his sunburnt chest and shoulders. His hair was cropped and his face a shiny brown. I'd never seen him in a shirt, but he wore a ragged pair of shorts from morn till night.

Lal and Jimmy grabbed their life-jackets, snatched up a couple of blankets and went to sleep on deck with Franco. The rest of us settled down in the bunks. Then a tremendous underwater explosion sent us rolling. Young Franco returned to the cabin, skin all shiny wet with sweat, white teeth gleaming in the dark. 'Someone's copped it!' he said. 'Better get topside.'

Eddie and Sam turned over and went to sleep.

'Let's go!' Franco said excitedly. 'The ocean's on fire! Grab a life-jacket. We're sitting ducks.'

It seemed the sensible thing to do, so I grabbed my life-preserver. 'Where's yours?' I asked the skinning boy.

'On deck. I'm using it for a fuckin' pillow. Come on!' he shouted. 'Bring a blanket. Sleep on deck. It's safer.'

Perspiration streamed from me. I grabbed my things and went topside with the stunning lad.

Scarlet flames came from the water, a film of blazing oil and debris. The convoy sailed on, the stars danced around the silvery moon and everyone settled down.

'Must have been a tanker,' said the young seaman. 'Jesus! Fancy swimming in that lot.'

He moved in close. In the shadows all around were curled-up bodies in twos and threes and singles. Franco's arm went round my shoulder. 'Let's share the blankets,' he said. 'I'm getting cold.'

'Well, piss off and get in your bunk,' I replied. 'Don't fuck about. They'll think we're a couple of queers.'

That seemed to be the end of it but not for the handsome lad. He sneaked beneath my blanket in the night, pressed his ragged-skinned chest to my back and his stiffened sex to my pants. A warm hand stroked my shoulder, so I gripped the wrist. 'Can't you take no for an answer?' I whispered. 'Now piss off!'

'I like you,' said the boy. 'I thought we were good friends.'

'We ain't that friendly,' I snapped. 'Do you think I'm a piece of fruit?'

'Don't take it so serious,' Franco whispered. 'You like me. I know you do. It's only a bit of bum.'

I could see the screaming pansies all around, hear the insulting remarks, sense the disgusting behaviour and wanted no part of it.

'What's up?' asked my bunk-mate.

'Nothing,' I said. 'Cheerio, kid. I'm going back to the cabin.'

He apologised the next morning and we became good shipmates.

The sailors, deck hands and ordinary seamen of the fo'c'sle had an afternoon ritual, an ancient custom handed down by generations of Chinese seafaring men, a tea break known as tab-nab time. Tab-nabs, a delicious confectionery, came up from the ship's galley at 3 p.m. each day and Franco got a special kick out of sharing his with me. We met each day, sat on the canvas-covered hatch and scoffed the mouth-watering cakes beneath the sun.

Franco's skin blew away in the wind, his lovely sex peeped from his ragged shorts and his golden body teased me with its fragrance. Still under shock from my exposure to the dreadful behaviour of the queers in the glory hole, I kept the lad at bay and remained just friends.

Table Mountain came up on the port bow, a wondrous sight, safe waters for the convoy and the first port of any significance. All silver trim and perfect tableau, the big ships gathered in the Cape Town bay, dancing lightly in the stream, slipping gentle bow waves, holding thousands of troops and sunburned sons of the sea. What a sight!

A woman stood on the quayside, a beautiful woman all dressed in white, her long black hair flying in the breeze with bunches of bright red roses in her arms, a smile on her lovely face and a wonderful voice that rang across the bay. She sang a welcome to South Africa, she sang the songs of home, and her voice reached out, touched the heart strings, echoed in the mountains and bounced right back like silver bells. Her repertoire seemed unlimited. Songs of the Welsh valley, songs of Ireland, songs of happiness and hope.

Thousands of servicemen lined the decks and tears ran down their sunburned cheeks. The voice reached into their souls — mamma's voice and sister's voice, the voice of those they'd left behind. It went on all through the day and far into the night, Yankee songs and Southern songs, hymns and prayers and 'Yiddische Momma'. She sang until every serviceman was safe ashore and finished off with the song of the Old Transvaal.

It was wonderful, patriotic, made the blood course through tthe veins, quickened the pulse and sent you off to liberate the oppressed, the poor and the victims of Nazi tyranny all over Europe. Freedom! Freedom! The liberating avengers are here!

The black-skinned natives weren't impressed. They'd heard it all before, and still awaited a knight in shining armour to set them free, let them ride on city transport or take a piss in the public pissholes of Durban, Cape Town, Port Elizabeth and all the other fine cities of God's own country. Whites only! Whites only!

Preparing five-course breakfasts, seven-course lunches and twelve-course dinners for the rich and famous had given me a taste for good food and wine, so I went ashore in Cape Town, found a high-class hotel and ordered the best meal that money could buy. It was delightful, served by smiling waiters and finished off with the golden-coloured brandy of the Cape. White-shirted, expensive shoes on my feet, well-cut trousers and an after-dinner glow, I left the posh establishment and felt that the sophistication of Jackie Robinson had begun.

Garry rides and rickshaw journeys, all the sights and sounds and smells of South Africa came to me. Clouds of gorgeous blossoms, the wonderful chant of the Zulu and the colourful ballet of the flamingo soaring through the sky.

A small trip round the coast to pick up a cargo and there was Durban, the most beautiful place on earth. Great ocean rollers to ride, baskets of delicious fruit to eat and sweet South African boys to kiss. They were lovely, all tiny shorts and long brown legs and gorgeous smiling faces. I promised myself to return one day, but meanwhile, what of the cargo?

The cargo was Italian war prisoners! Human beings were called a cargo. Cargo below decks, hatches battened down and fast, the *Antenor* joined a homeward-bound convoy and set sail for Glasgow, the tail o' the bank. Hands reached up from below decks, poked through the wooden grill of the hatches and signalled for attention. They wanted simple things like spoons and metal objects they could carve and twist into ornamental jewelry. Their skills were quite amazing and the finished articles absolutely breathtaking.

Some prisoners gave an undertaking and were released on parole, given a simple task to perform during the voyage. There weren't too many parolees but among the few was a fat young man named Alberto, a friendly guy with a wife and two young kids in Naples. He worked in the saloon galley, spoke very little English and said yes to everything. Alberto prepared breakfast with me, cooked tasty omelettes, ate enough for ten men and had rubber-lined pockets for sealing extra rations which he gave to his locked-up comrades. My mates made gallons of surplus coffee just to watch him perform.

Transporting prisoners was distasteful, and made us realise the madness of war. I'm sure my mates and I would have helped them escape if the opportunity had presented itself. Sad music and song came from the hatches and the sun blistered the decks. Alberto turned the handle of a mincing machine and I stuffed it with chunks of raw beef. He was teaching me an Italian song when my thumb got trapped in the mincer.

I screamed too late. Alberto reversed the action, released my mangled thumb and fainted at the sight of the torn flesh. What a mess! I couldn't tell which was thumb and which was beef. The ship's doctor wanted to amputate. Fortunately, there was a famous surgeon aboard, an Italian prisoner-of-war who'd offered his services to the ship's company. He was brilliant and thought the new sulpha drugs could save the damaged thumb.

The winds of war had brought great changes in the field of medicine. New miracle drugs were in common use on the battlefields of the world but had not yet reached the civilian population. I heard so much about them that I almost forgot the pain. It was a tremendous moment for me when the surgeon said, 'Typhus and tuberculosis will be stamped out along with almost every known disease.'

'When? When?'

'Tomorrow, the next day. Who knows? Venereal disease is under complete control and can be cured in a matter of hours.'

He stitched me up, stuffed me with miracle drugs and sent me off duty for the remainder of the voyage. Things went well for a couple of days. Arm in a sling, the new drugs at work in my system, I spent the time in a pair of shorts and sunbathed near the after poop deck. Franco watched over me, brought my meals and nursed me when the fever came.

It was a nightmare! I raved and perspired, tossed about, Franco in and out of my dreams, a cloak of dreadful pain and sickness.

It was dark. We lay at anchor off the west coast of Africa, a million stars overhead, the smell of palms and spices on the breeze.

'You've come round,' Franco said. 'Jesus! You've been out for days. How you feeling now, Jacko?'

'Fine,' I said. 'Did they cut my thumb off?'

He washed me down, brushed my hair, dried me with his towel. The throbbing pain left me, gone, washed away with Franco's tender care. A plaster of Paris, bloodstained and dirty, showed the thumb still secure and part of me.

'How long have I slept on deck?' I enquired.

'A few days,' replied my mate. 'Wanna smoke?'

'Yeah, sure. Thanks kid. Thanks for everything.'

He brought a fresh blanket, tucked me in, stuffed a pillow beneath my head.

'Okay, Jacko?'

'Wonderful! Are you bunking down with me?'

'I've been with you all week,' he said. 'I slept under your blanket and held you in my arms. You asked me to hold you close. Don't you remember?'

'I dunno, Franco, but I think I'm a bit of a cry baby at times.'

He had the smooth-skinned fragrance of youth, the smell of boy about him, a delicious aroma that filled my nostrils with pleasure. His eyes were wide apart, long and sloping, the eyes of adolescence, artless, simple and very sincere. A comely boy, bonny and well-favoured, his polished skin glistened beneath the starry sky.

Franco didn't need an invitation, knew instinctively that he was welcome and dragged his ragged shorts off. A tiny pair of snow-white knickers clung to his bottom, bulged at the front and looked breathtakingly beautiful against his dark brown tan. He made love like an expert.

'Why did we have to wait so long?' he asked. 'You're a fruit, and you know it. We could be great shipmates.'

Sucking his lovely big penis and trying to explain that I wasn't a queer seemed ridiculous, so I just accepted the love that passed between us and hoped he wouldn't talk about it with the other guys.

A little excitement came our way at Gibraltar, nothing spectacular, just a few escaping prisoners in the night. The fortunate escapees weren't from the *Antenor* but we wished them well and hoped they'd make it to the safety of the Spanish shore.

A few days later, we skirted the bay of Biscay and followed the convoy home. Glasgow seemed as good a place to pay off as any, so I took my discharge. I'd certainly enjoyed my first trip, wished to remain with the Blue Funnel Company, but carrying prisoners had disturbed me, so I decided to change vessels.

Jimmy and Franco hadn't reached a decision. They took their pay, a fortnight's shore leave, and boarded the Liverpool-bound express train with me. Franco lived in the Midlands and wanted to join his family as soon as possible. The pubs were open when we reached Liverpool, so we rolled into the Legs of Man on Lime Street, had a farewell drink and promised to meet again at the Company office in Birkenhead. Perhaps we'd all sail together once more. They'd been good shipmates, but I wanted a much stronger relationship, someone who could share my life as well as the exciting sea voyages.

The Lime Street alehouse known as the Legs of Man was nothing special, just an old-fashioned pub with spit and sawdust on the deck and blackout curtains at the entrance. It seemed as good a place as any to meet my friends, but more than that they were men of the sea, salt-water men, and I was one of them at last.

I'd only been in the joint five minutes when Jimmy Mack walked in and ordered a round of drinks. A Yankee sailor joined us, a regular seafaring guy, dark-blue pea jacket, shaven head, very tight pants and slip-on shoes.

'Just blew in from the Argentine,' he said. 'Can I buy you guys a drink?'

'Why not?' said Jim. 'Those vigilantes still running round B.A. with swords?'

'The cops?' replied the Yank. 'You can say that again. They see a goddam bum on the streets, they belt his ass with a sabre!'

'Well,' I said, trying to get in with a little salt-water talk, 'I suppose that cuts down the number of bums in Buenos Aires. You ever been to West Africa?'

'Never,' said the Yank.

'It's a friggin' eyesore,' Jimmy said like an oldtimer. 'Fucken' big palm trees waving in the breeze, bum boats all over the fucken' waterfront.'

'Bum boats?' enquired the Yank.

'A fucken' boat full of geezers on the bum.'

'Plenty a bums on the Bowery,' replied the Yankee sailor. 'Noo York's the place for bums an' I ain't kidding.'

Fortunately, one of Jimmy's uncles came into the bar and put an end to the intellectual discussion on bums. Uncle Mack had spent a lot of time in India and most of his life at sea. His friends called him Doolali Tap, a kind of pun on the state of his mental properties. Doolali seemed to be a place in India where most of the residents were slightly tapped. Nevertheless, Uncle Mack appeared reasonably well balanced at the moment. A medium-built guy with thinning hair, lots of brylcreem, forty-five years old and a house full of teenage kids.

'What yo gonna drink?' asked the Yank.

'Scotch,' replied Uncle Mack. 'You from Noo York.'

'You can say that again!' said the sailor, shoving his gum in the side of his mouth.

Uncle Mack might have been a bit tapped but he wasn't daft, so he knocked back his scotch and said, 'Cheers!' The conversation resumed its remarkable level of intelligence and after a while Uncle Mack invited us to a late-night party in his prefab.

'There's a load of booze up at the house,' he said, 'but we might as well take some of this scotch while we can get it. Johnny Walker is hard to come by.'

The Yank seemed to take it as a compliment so he bought a couple of bottles, stuffed them in his pea jacket and went outside to hail a cab. We all piled in and drove to Huyton-with-Roby, the overspill for bombed-out Merseyside families. Most of Jimmy's relatives lived on the same estate and were housed in chalet homes, prefabricated houses shipped in from Canada and constructed on site, screwed in place like a leggo set and just as colourful.

It was common knowledge that a good many houses had been destroyed in Liverpool, but the extent of the damage hadn't registered with me until I saw the new housing estates. Sparkling toy towns would be a fair description. Whole communities had grown like mushrooms overnight, complete with electric mains, drainage, gas, traffic lights, footpaths and cycle paths. There would never be a housing shortage again. Everything was under control and extremely well organised.

The taxi set us down outside Uncle Mack's bungalow and we paid off the driver.

'What a place!' I said to Jim. It must be great living here.'

It was beautiful. Neat little gardens, modern, steel-framed windows, bedrooms, living-room, dining-room and kitchen, central heating, back-to-back fireplace complete with gas poker, ultra-modern bathroom and plenty of family space. A coal house and cycle shed could be seen in most back gardens and a few garages here and there. Flowers, shrubs, young trees and wire-mesh fencing separated the bungalows and created a peaceful setting.

The families in Huyton-with-Roby were from every part of the city, but the majority seemed to be docklanders: whole streets and neighbourhoods transplanted and given a second chance. Until recently, a family income was limited to about three pounds a week. Now, however, it was more like ten pounds a head, an outrageous sum of money. Shift workers, girls on munitions and a thousand other wartime occupations didn't know what to do with their cash. They spent a lot on their comfortable new homes. Shiny electric toasters, electric kettles and flashy radios appeared and brightened up their lives.

Manufacturers produced as many goods as possible, spread the raw materials to the limit, cut the standard sizes, altered the designs and filled the shops with poor-quality goods known as utility ware. The housewives went on a spending spree, filling the little homes with utility beds, utility sideboards and thin utility carpets. Utility cups came on the scene, no handles and no glaze, utility forks had only three prongs and the knives were designed without handles. Manufacturers cut the costs, raised the prices and doubled their profits while the boom lasted.

Millions of pots and pans were collected from family homes. Park railings, garden fences and cast-iron rails from public buildings were taken for scrap and filled a hole in the profiteer's economy. Nothing was spared. On with the show, the greatest show on earth! Stung again, Joe!

The family purse remained full, so they did their best to empty it in the pubs. Glasses were still around but not too many. The Yanks tried to ease the situation by drinking from the bottle. Actually, that's what they'd been advised to do, as the native Englishman had dirty drinking habits and pub glasses were rinsed in the same water all through the evening. Nevertheless, the publicans helped out by substituting jam-jars for beer glasses, and some even changed the water in the sink from time to time.

The toy towns were known for their free and easy ways, rowdy drinking parties and all-night knees-ups. Uncle Mack's comfortable residence was one of the liveliest.

'Keep away from my cousins,' warned Jimmy. 'They're all in the pudden' club and just looking for a guy like you to put the blame on. There's gonna be some fun when the British army come home and find millions of babies chewing gum and scoffin' Coca-Cola.'

The girls didn't look like members of any special club, but the US NCOs' club was just down the road in Huyton, a notorious place of racial warfare: US whites versus US blacks. There was no racial prejudice in Uncle Mack's home, all kinds of Americans had been invited to the party. Seafaring families were not very sophisticated, but they had some common sense.

Common sense, however, didn't prevent everyone from getting blind drunk and crashing out all over the house, bodies in the bedrooms, hallway and bathroom and flaked out on the living-room carpet. Young Josie Mack got far too close for comfort so, with Jimmy's warning words on my mind, I rolled away from the girl, moved towards the fire and bedded down for the last few hours.

A smell of spearmint gum came floating near my nostrils and a warm body moved close, an exciting male body. The firelight dwindled, the masculine frame moved closer and touched me. No hand appeared, nothing, just the warmth and the pressure and the fragrant smell. The situation aroused me sexually, so I turned to face the exciting person and wondered who it could be. Someone climbed across the sleeping crowd, opened the front door and went outside. A sound of running water came to my ears, then the prowler returned, and everyone settled down in the blacked-out living-room.

Firm stomach muscles touched, trousered knees and stockinged feet came together. My sleeping companion was excited and knew perfectly well that I was feeling sexy. A hand stroked my face, a gentle hand, soft and youthful, the skin as warm as toast. I cupped his chin in my palm, felt the smooth touch of boy's flesh, soft and fresh and very cool, a beautiful sensation that brought my blood to the boil, made my heart beat faster.

'Alex?' I enquired, lips at the smooth-skinned cheek. Alex was another of Jimmy's cousins, but at least he was no member of the pudden' club.

'Yes,' came a whispered reply. His sweet young lips accepted my kiss, a gentle kiss, the kiss of man and boy. He tasted of chocolate biscuits and smelt of Wrigley's gum. Fingers touching, bodies warm and close, we hung on till the dawn sneaked through the edge of the blackout curtain, when sleep crept up and closed our weary eyes.

A few guests had departed when we awoke and made our way outside.

'What are you doing today?' asked Alex.

'I'm going riding,' I said, 'but I'll have to go home first. I need to wash and clean up.'

'I only live across the way,' Alex said. 'You can get washed in my place. Where are we going riding?'

'Over the water, Hoylake sands. Can you ride?'

'No I can't,' said the boy. 'You can teach me. It should be fun. How much does it cost, by the way?'

'Five bob an hour.'

Uncle Mack's bathroom had been busy for the past hour, so I was glad of the boy's offer. He had two teenage sisters and they were getting ready for work when we walked in the house. His mother, a trousered tram conductress, was eating a piece of buttered toast. 'There's money on the sideboard,' she said with her mouth full. 'Get some dinner in Woolworth's cafeteria.'

'Leave me another quid,' said the lad. 'I'm going riding this afternoon.'

'Riding!' she exclaimed. 'Horse riding? You'll fall off and break your bloody neck.'

'Don't act daft,' replied her son. 'They're tired old riding-school ponies, rocking horses. Anyone can ride them. Ask Jack.'

'I'm going to be late for work,' she answered, swallowing a mouthful of tea. 'Be careful, dear.'

His sisters looked like all the other girls in Huyton, zip-sided trousers, turban-wrapped head, high-heeled shoes, plenty of make-up slapped on and well rubbed down, Max Factor eyelashes, painted nails. They looked like female impersonators. They were scorned in the press for their trousers; they were banned from the jazz halls, barred from the boozers, but wore their trousers with pride and wouldn't give in. I wasn't really interested in women's trousers. There were more important things on my mind.

Alex and I took the Mersey railway to Hoylake, hired a couple of hunters and set off down a country lane. The boy's mount stopped and munched at some grass in the pathside. 'It won't go!' he shouted. 'What shall I do?'

'Hit the fucken' thing.'

'What with?'

I tore a small branch from a nearby bush. 'Pull his head back,' I suggested.

Alex took up the reins and I gave the cunning old nag a slash with the twigs. That did the trick. He went galloping down the lane, Alex screaming with laughter and hanging on, hands, knees and bumps-a-daisy.

It went on for days, a real courtship, riding every afternoon, holding hands in the evening cinema show, snatching a kiss behind his bedroom door.

Alex was a fine young schoolboy, awaiting acceptance by the Gravesend sea school, the training establishment for merchant navy lads. The family threw a farewell party for him, just another lively night. Everyone knew we were close, very close. Alex and Jack, Jack and Alex, the names went together like bacon and egg.

The night was cool, his room warm and comfortable. A wax candle lit the chamber, the guttering flame of the light casting our shadows, making the eyes gleam; lights flickered and danced mischievously in his pupils. Alex wanted me, wished to share his secrets, exchange kisses, the feather-light kisses of boys who love men; mere touches of tender skin and soft lips. He'd chosen me instinctively, knew I would understand and trusted me implicitly. Everything was ready for us — the long night, the warm and friendly bed, the pleasure in our eyes. He clasped his hands round my neck and smiled into my face, an exciting youth, waiting, waiting.

The sexual strength flowed between us. Our mouths met again, lips parted, a sexual kiss of acceptance, flesh into virgin flesh, a journey into the unknown. Alex wanted more than kisses, though. His searching fingers reached into my pants and held me for the first time. His shirt came away in my hands and our naked chests came together, all squeaky skin and quivering breasts. Cheek to cheek, lips nuzzled into sensitive spots beneath the neck and near the ears, into soft and fragrant hair.

No sounds disturbed us in the night, the soft light from the paraffin wax all around, dancing on the wall, flickering in the mirrored wardrobe. Content to hold and exchange kisses, we lay face to face, hands clasped. Bursting with muscular tissue and hardened sex, we reached the point of no return. He wanted total love and so did I.

Alex sat upon the pillow, felt my hungry lips and gave me his exciting flesh to taste. Aladdin's wonderful cave, unknown pathways, walls tight and closing in, right into the forbidden territory, heavy burden screaming to be released. The brilliant treasure spills from the sack and leaves its gleaming jewels all around.

'I just wanted to please you.'

'I wanted to make you happy.'

We hug and kiss.

He will make the journey out tomorrow. A twelve-week course at the sea school will separate us, but we know that we will meet again in Toytown and some day sail the seas together.

7. Johnny Fortune's 'Tyndareus'

It was one of those Merseyside mornings, green and grey and friggin' windy, one of those periods between sunrise and sunset when you can't tell spring from winter or the autumn from the summer and everybody says it's a lousy day. The tank was running low, nothing in the kick to jingle, time to ship out and earn some cash.

Bing Crosby had just made it big with a number called 'Sunday, Monday or Always'. The words from the popular hit ran through my mind as I boarded the ferry for Birkenhead. 'Won't you tell me when . . . we will meet again . . . Sunday . . . Monday . . .'

There was no one special in my life, nobody to dream about, not a soul to say goodbye. I wasn't the lonely type but I needed someone desperately. I guess I missed my army mates and the wonderful feeling of comradeship.

Across the old grey Mersey, big ships anchored in the stream, busy little tug boats at work, the waterways alive and bustling. My own little world, my boyhood dreams come true. What lovely vessel awaited me? What wondrous voyage lay before me? Most important of all: what exciting shipmates would I find?

'All ashore for Birkenhead,' shouted an old-timer. 'Woodside Birkenhead! Step lively there!'

The office manager at the Blue Funnel — an ex-skipper, pencil behind the ear, grey beard, no hair on his shiny head, dark blue civilian suit, black neck-tie, polished boots, grey-green eyes — looked up from his untidy desk and smiled at me.

'Shipping out?' he asked.

'Yes sir!' I replied. 'What have you got?'

The *S.S. Tyndareus*, he said, chewing the end of his pencil. 'She's tied up here in Birkenhead. Go take a look at her. She's sailing in a few days.'

'Is she a trooper?' I asked.

'No,' he said, putting the bitten pencil on the desk. 'She's an intermediary vessel, a ship that carries passengers and cargo. Got a fair-sized crew and a ship's doctor.'

A few more guys entered the office. They seemed to be signing on the *Tyndareus*, so I joined them and came away with a £20 advance note — a promissory note made out by the Blue Funnel Shipping Company and accepted as paper money in most parts of the world. Unfortunately, you had to buy goods with the advance note. Ship's chandlers made the transactions and gave you change in cash. There were others: sharks who hung around the dock gates and bought the notes. These people took a good percentage for themselves, four shillings in the pound. I passed them by and took the ferry to Liverpool.

Crowds of shipbuilders and servicemen came aboard the ferry. There was something special and exciting about the atmosphere they generated. Perhaps it was the ship itself, the *Royal Daffodil*. Merseysiders had crossed the water on the old tub ever since I could remember. She'd sailed into Dunkirk and taken survivors from the beaches. Young lovers crossed the water in her, played guitars and sang the courting songs of youth. Ropes as thick as a man's leg curled and coiled about the scrubbed decks, gleaming engines could be clearly seen by the passengers, and steel-railed gangways cluttered the lower deck.

'The Pier Head!' shouted an ancient mariner. 'Stand by for the Pier Head!' Stand by was exactly what they did. Passengers braced themselves, leaned forward from the waist, feet flat on the deck, eyes focussed on the floating pier, awaiting the bump as the *Royal Daffodil* hit the landing stage with a thump and sent the message home: 'The Pier Head!'

White water bubbled from beneath the screw, foaming, rushing, gurgling white water like soapy suds on wash-day. Insurance ropes went over the side and kids stood fascinated as the ferrymen tied up, bent the powerful ropes round the stanchions, slid the heavy gangways into place and watched the busy Merseysiders bustle ashore.

The floating pier was lined with empty slot machines for Nestle's milk chocolate, penny a bar. When would they fill them up again? What price would the milky bars cost when the time came? It looked like the end of the penny bar of chocolate, a sad moment for all the scruffy kids who played around the waterfront.

The crowds climbed up the steep slopes of the outer gangways, the glass-roofed footwalks that led from floating pier to terra firma. Hundreds of tramcars awaited them, Crawford's Cream Crackers on the front, Oxo, Lifebuoy soap emblazoned on the sides, the Bisto kids on the back.

The gleaming rails of the tramway shimmered in the dirty street. The monstrous Liver bird looked down as Mr and Mrs Liverpool climbed aboard the Corporation transport.

'Fares please!' bawled the uniformed conductress. I offered two pennies for Tuebrooke. She looked at my badge.

'No charge for seamen!' she said and made me feel like a king.

Jamie was away. North Africa perhaps, his mother said, but wasn't sure. Timmy had settled into a flat with his friend Andy, a compact little place above a garage. We were all growing up. It bothered me. I didn't want to grow up without Jamie. I couldn't get him out of my mind. His mother's soft Lancashire voice filled my ear, sent shivers of happiness up and down my spine, so I sent her a kiss on the blower.

I packed a couple of grips, good handmade leather bags I'd bought in Africa. Jamie's forty-five gleamed blue and oily on my windowsill, so I slung it in a bag, grabbed a handful of rimless ammunition, tied it in a paisley scarf and threw it in with the gear. Something told me I'd need it, need to stay alive. It felt good. I picked up the gun, hefted it, gave it a quick spin, broke out the magazine and filled it with shells.

They were all 'out there': Jamie, Duffy, Clithero and gentle Rodney. I hoped we'd meet again out there, that mysterious place we talked about. Where and what the hell was 'out there'?

Whatever it was, I knew I was on my way to meet it. I just wished there was someone close, someone who could take my hand when I needed it, give me a kiss before I closed my eyes.

A tramcar took me into town. I wanted to smell Lime Street before I left the old city, so I parked my bags and cruised the pavement. A French flying officer bought me a drink in Yate's wine lodge. He was smooth, good-looking, and fancied a fine young sailor boy. I bought him a glass of Spanish red and we drank a toast to General De Gaulle. I wouldn't go to the men's room with him. He must have been thirty years old, far too old for me.

He went to the cloakroom and I knocked back a glass of old douro. I went outside, peeped through the window and saw the Frenchman search the bar. He spied a young American soldier and moved in, two glasses of vino in his hands, a special look in his eye. Bonne chance! Vive la France!

A last look at the Forum, a few steps into the Futurist, the movie house where I'd met so many lovely friends in my early years. Over to St John's market, the smell of fresh cod and smoked haddocks in my nostrils. Who was St John? What was his connection with the sea ports of the world?

Blood and sawdust underfoot. 'Fine young rabbits!' shouted the market traders. 'There's a lovely conger eel?'

The button boots of the Mary Ellens shone like glass. They still wore the street-trader's shawl, and they still raised their long print skirts and pissed in the back entries and jiggers of stinking Merseyside.

'Fine ripe American apples! No coupons needed for fresh fruit!'

That made me think. Had a ship actually crossed the Atlantic, dodged the minefields and run the U-boat gauntlet, just to sail into Liverpool with a cargo of tuppenny apples? It didn't make sense.

The pawnshops in Park Road were busy, so it must have been Thursday evening. Friday night is pay night. Mill Street and Park Road fascinated me — the smell of poor people, the ting-tong music of Chinatown, the smell of rope and docks and warehouse stabling.

Through the long steep streets, coloured music, jazzy and black, soul sounds from the open windows, the high-stepped dwellings of the heart of Liverpool. Guinness, the blood of Merseyside, slopped over the bar-room tables. Kids played pitch and toss and nearest to the wall.

A last sniff. So long Liverpool!

I knew she was going to be a trouble ship when I first set eyes on the trimmers and firemen with their belt buckles in the small of the back, shanghai jeans and dirty, chain-breaker singlets - the international uniform of the coal-burning 'black gangs'. Bastards, every one of them! Trouble followed in their wake like driftwood after a storm.

The *Tyndareus* had been around the oceans of the world for more than twenty years, a real Clydesider, the biggest cargo vessel afloat, eleven hatches on her holy-stoned decks and a wooden-slatted spud locker perched atop the galley like Uncle Tom's cabin. The guys in the catering department seemed reasonable enough — a butcher from Sydney, a few friendly Merseysiders and a stunning lad named Pete from Western Australia. The skipper was Captain Fortune, a company man with a reputation for discipline and for being a mean bastard when it came to shore leave.

I slung my grip in an empty bunk, helped myself to a cigarette from a tin of fifty that was looking lonely on the cabin table, struck a match and lit up. Butch and Pete were my cabin mates, so I guess one of them owned the tin of smokes.

Pete came in from the shower, towel about his waist. Water ran down his neck, trickled down his sun-burned back, dribbled over a shapely chest. The magic was there!

'Got any dough?' he smiled.'

'I've got a twenty-quid advance note.'

'Yeah! I gotta hundred American dollars,' he said. 'You wanna come ashore for a beer?'

A fascinating boy with a colorful butterfly tattooed on a meaty buttock, Pete climbed into a pair of shorts and dragged them up around his waist.

'Suits me, but I'll have to cash this advance note.'

'See Butch,' said the butterfly boy. 'He'll cash your note and won't take a cut.'

Butch was a big bony guy, a real Sydneysider and a mine of information, most of it about dames and the whores of the waterfronts all over the world. He wore a soft hat, a shirt and tie, a well-pressed lounge suit and looked more like a Hollywood gangster than a seafarer. He took the company money, handed me twenty pounds and slipped the advance note in with his roll.

'If you kids wanna good time,' he said out of the side of his mouth, 'go to the Ocean Club. No old dolls, no clap, good music and a lousy restaurant.'

Pete wore zip-fronted pants, a button-down shirt, white socks, slip-on loafers, real Stateside gear. He was a smouldering beauty, clear brown skin, stardust in his dark brown eyes, dancing lights in his shiny black hair. Head erect and shoulders square, he knew he was attractive. Long slim legs ate up the pavement, a tremulous motion beneath the seat of his pants. Pete had a glow about him that turned the head, something very special. People stared as he walked by.

I hoped to visit America, to buy some modern clothes like the zip trousers, jacket-type shirts and colourful gear that only US servicemen and seamen wore. 'Where do you think we're bound?' I asked my companion.

'Who knows?' replied Pete. 'She won't be ready for a coupla days. Maybe we'll get some information when we join the convoy.'

'You been to New York?'

'Lots of times. Have you?'

'No,' I answered quickly. 'Only sailed in one ship, a trooper.'

'I made all kinds of trips in all sorts of ships,' said Pete. 'I'll show you around if we hit the Big Apple.'

In and out of a few downtown bars, grabbing a bite to eat in a Lime Street milk bar, servicemen shoulder to shoulder, jostling, pushing . . .

'Hey baby! Ham sandwich anna glassa milk. Goddam it!'

We made our way to the Ocean Club, the most cosmopolitan of nightclubs, the focal point and meeting-place for seamen and uniformed Americans. Loaded jeeps buzzed up and down the main stem. Yanks dropped off and met their friends and moved in and out of the swing doors from dawn to dawn. It seemed very

Americanised and extremely popular. A smell of masculine deodorants and fresh linen, the clean scent of Americans, fragrant bodies, a new bouquet for the English nose to savour.

Bottled lager seemed to be in great demand. Carlsberg, something the American boys had brought into town. I'd never seen it before, but then I wasn't very sophisticated.

'Noisy bastards the Yanks!'

'I like 'em.'

'So do I,' replied Pete. 'You wanna hit the dance floor?'

'Why not? You staying out all night or are you gonna sleep aboard ship?'

'I'm easy,' said Pete.

We grabbed a couple of girls and moved our bodies to the magic of Glenn Miller. 'Twelfth Street Rag' came up and the polished ballroom floor bounced. We moved along with the seething crowd of jitterbuggers. But the atmosphere was that of war.

'I got some friends in town, Pete. We could stay with them if you like,' I said as we sat one out.

He looked around and waved his hand at the crowd of bright young people, strange uniforms, foreign voices, sweating faces and laughing eyes. 'This is what I like,' he said.

Things cooled down about two in the morning.

'Guess we better find some place to crash out,' said Pete. 'A hotel or one of those joints near the railway station. I don't fancy creeping round the docks at this hour. Let's go!'

The city buzzed with life — taxis and crowded jeeps, drunken servicemen and girls, bottles of whisky at the hip, drunken drivers all and proud of it, the indifference of youthful warriors showing clearly on their adolescent faces.

The Adelphi, Liverpool's finest hotel, home of the rich and famous, catered for the elite: US majors, colonels and general staff. Officers, young and handsome, fat and flabby, cigar-smoking plutocrats and a new generation of happy-go-lucky captains and lieutenants filled the lounge and sat around in a cloud of tobacco smoke: Philip Morris, Lucky Strike, Old Gold and Camel. The US valise, a kind of folding canvas wardrobe, was a very popular piece of officer equipment. Porters carried them in and out, up and down, a hive of activity, a nomadic procession from reception desk to elevator and back again.

Ordinary Joes weren't welcome in the Adelphi so we crept away and joined a few turkeys and dog-faces in the lounge of a less fashionable hotel. The night porter gave us a room, booked us down for a breakfast call, the *Daily Mirror*, an early cup of tea. He took our money and Pete took the room key, ordering a pot of coffee in the lounge and two stiff drinks while we waited.

We sank into a couple of ancient armchairs, soft and rich with velvet, high wings each side to keep away the draughts. The snoozing lounge lizards of yesterday certainly knew the value of comfortable hotel furniture.

'Good health!' Pete said when the drinks came up. 'You know we got ourselves a double room, don't you?'

'So?'

'Not a twin, a double.'

'What's the difference?' I asked.

'Only one bed.'

'Well that's alright,' I said. 'I'm used to sleeping with another guy. I spent half my life sharing my friend's room.'

'Just thought I'd mention it,' remarked Pete. 'I guess we're lucky to get a room of any kind. Looks like the US Army has come to town on the piss. Must be the fourth of fuckin' July.'

The coffee came up on a silver tray. A friendly waiter on the night staff filled the cups, smiled when he received a tip and walked off with his calf-length tails trailing in the breeze.

'Nice joint,' Pete said. 'We'd better do this again. I had a great time tonight. I love all this crap. We go well together, Jack. Did you enjoy yourself?'

'Wonderful! This puts the icing on the cake. I feel like a rich dude. I'd love to have another night out with you before the ship sails.'

Pete looked serious. He held out his hand. 'We should be together for a long time,' he said quietly. 'These fuckin' cargo boats go out for years.'

I took his hand, and we gripped quite firmly.

'Shipmates?' he asked.

'Nothing I'd like better, Pete. I keep losing my friends. It's the war. My real mate is in the army. We were together since we were kids. I could use a reliable pal, a guy I can depend on. Someone who'll stick with me. You know what I mean.'

'Yeah, sure,' he replied. 'Let's hit the sack.' He looked at the tag on the key. 'Room 28,' he said. 'Where the hell's that?'

We found it on the first floor, a neat little chamber with everything for the weary traveller — clean linen, fresh towels, and a sliding door that led to a spotless bathroom and shower. Pete cleaned his teeth with his forefinger and toilet soap, not my style at all. I washed my hands, sponged my face, took a pee and returned to the bedroom. Standing in front of the wardrobe mirror, I stripped down to my knickers and admired myself while Pete removed his clothes, revealing a big erection, long and ready for anything. I stared at it.

'You always slept with your friend?' he asked, reaching out his hand. He touched my fingertips, a naked boy in all his natural splendour.

'Always,' I agreed.

'Like this?' he said softly. 'Did you always sleep like this?'

I slipped out of my shorts, climbed into bed, stretched out, face in the pillow. His hand ran gently down my spine, slid over my bare bottom.

'What's wrong?' he asked.'

'Nothing. Very masculine boys make me blush. I'll be alright in a minute.'

Pete took my face in his hands. 'Don't be shy with me,' he said. I smiled, held him close, felt his lips at my cheek, his hard flesh at my belly. The physical movements came naturally, the tender actions of boys who love boys.

His lips moved down my belly. 'What do you think of boys who suck each other?' he asked.

'It disturbs me,' I admitted. 'Makes me feel ashamed, but I did it with my friend because I loved him.'

He kissed the parts that attracted him. 'We can love each other,' he said quietly.

I knew he cared for me when we set out on a sweet-tasting act of love, sucked at the stiffened flesh, exchanged the most intimate kisses, sat on the bed and hugged, two simple lads in love. His face was flushed and damp. I wiped his shiny forehead with a corner of the sheet.

'We have to live together on a ship,' I reminded him.

It made no difference. I wanted him inside me and he knew it. We shared a pillow, Pete at my side, his warm breath on my shoulder and ready to take me, penis long and very hard. I took the beautiful thing and guided it to the special place for boys who seduce boys. He hugged me into his warm belly, gave me his hard body and his love right inside me.

'I wanted you all evening,' he said softly. 'Is it alright?'

'Yes. I wanted you.'

'Like this?'

'I just want to be with you, Pete, want to please you.'

'You're affectionate,' he said, 'The quiet kind, the kind of boy I want. I wasn't sure at first but I am now. Will you be my friend? I need someone close who understands me.'

'That's how it is with me,' I replied. 'I've always had a boyfriend, a guy who loved me. I need a boy I can rely on. It's not easy. Too many things go wrong, the war, every friggin' thing. You're just right for me, Pete.'

I knew what he wanted when he nuzzled into my belly. His lips were soft and teasing. They closed over me. I held his tousled head and watched him suck me all the way.

'I had to do that,' he admitted. 'I just had to. That's the way I am. Can't help it, I guess.'

'It's okay,' I said. 'You love me, don't you?'

'Very much,' he replied. 'We've got something, Jack, something I wanted for a long time.'

We moved in close, held tight, snuggled under the blankets, two happy, homosexual boys, madly in love.

A ship like the *Tyndareus* has four officers: the captain, and the first, second and third mates, sometimes referred to as first, second and third officers. The captain and his three mates run the ship. Down below in the engine-room are three other officers: chief engineer, second engineer and third engineer. The engineers are just that. They don't manage the ship's crew or take part in any discipline. They run the engines. The radio room also has three officers: first sparks, second sparks and junior sparks. They work the radio room, and are usually very young guys with no knowledge of seamen whatsoever. The 'black gang' — stokers, firemen, coal trimmers and donkeymen — shovel coal into the fires for the boilers that turn the engines.

The *Tyndareus* had used Chinese trimmers and firemen in the past, cheap labour they picked up on the South China coast. But there weren't too many Chinese about now; there were no trips there because of the war in the Far East. Not only that, but cheap labour wasn't so cheap any more. A war risk bonus of ten pounds a month had to be paid to all crew members.

Whatever the reason, the chief engineer didn't like the switch-over to English stokers and their mates. He stood at the top of the gangway at seven o'clock on the morning the ship was to sail and counted his drunken black gang crawling aboard.

Most of the crew were turned to, up and about and waiting to cast off. Being the junior member of the galley, I was peeling spuds on deck, not such a bad job as it sounds. It gave me the opportunity to sit around with my shirt off, something I enjoyed. The salt wind kept my skin alive, kept it fresh and brown. A couple of tattoos showed, nothing to be proud of, just one of those things that young guys do; camouflage, I guess, a means of throwing people off the scent.

It didn't hide me from Matt Jordan, one of the black gang. A real handsome bastard, he was maybe twenty-two years old, with a husky chest, gleaming teeth, sharp haircut and one of those tight-fitting tee-shirts that filled with muscle and exaggerated the body beneath the cotton fabric. His pants were tight and fitted well, a cool customer. Matt sat beside me and picked up a knife.

'I like peeling spuds,' he said.'

'No fooling!'

'Yeah! I was a galley boy for a couple of years. Should have been a cook. I liked the kitchens.'

'Then why did you give it up?' I asked.'

'Lots of reasons,' he said quietly. 'Now I work down below. It's alright, I guess. More exciting.'

He peeled a few more potatoes, talked about the different ships he'd sailed on and tried to make friends. 'Maybe we can go ashore for a few beers together,' he said. 'I'm sailing with a strange crew and I don't know any of the guys.'

'Why not?' I replied. 'It's alright by me.'

Matt put the knife down. 'See ya around,' he said. 'You know where to find me if you need a friend.'

'Yeah, sure, Matt. See ya.'

We sailed into the North Atlantic that night, a huge convoy, big ships stretching out as far as the eye could see. Destroyers tossed about like kids' toys, a great wilderness of grey-green water. Ships were lost from sight in the trough of a forty-foot wave and bounced right back on the crest of a western ocean roller. They looked as if they'd never survive the trip.

My mates were all around me, a terrific bunch of stewards, cooks, pantrymen and clerks. Pete worked in the pantry. Butch, my other cabin mate, had his own domain, the butcher shop. Everyone liked him, the most popular guy aboard. The departments were absolutely separated. Black gang aft, sailors in the fo'c'sle, catering staff midships. Consequently, I hardly knew the rest of the crew.

From time to time I spotted a filthy-looking trimmer or fireman, usually creeping from a hole in the deck, bag of dirt and cinders on a skinny shoulder. Clinkering, they called it. The hole in the deck was called a fiddley and the stinking bowels of the ship were called the engine room. God know what they called the hold where the black gang sweated at the shovels. Hell, I guess. It was like a coal mine, hundreds of tons of coal, naked stokers. They started the watch in filthy jeans, belt buckles so hot they were worn at the small of the back because they burned the wrist and forearm.

Water boys, firemen's peggies, carried buckets of sea water, tossed the icy liquid over the naked body of a team mate then returned to the sea-water tap for more. Fresh water was too precious, hosepipes too dangerous. The guys used salt-water soap to clean the grime away. Ordinary soap wouldn't lather.

I could never figure out the name peggy. There were ship's peggies, sailor's peggies, a bosun's peggy and a fireman's peggy. Words and names interested me but this one was always elusive. I suppose you could call the kid an apprentice, but in nautical terms an apprentice is an officer cadet.

Trimmers, wiry little guys with barrows, fed the stokers with fuel and trimmed the mountains of coal. An uneven trim meant loss of stability, a list to one side and loss of seaway, the speed at which the vessel travelled.

Trimmers, firemen and peggies worked in teams, sailed the seas together and survived by one another's sweat and skill. They got drunk and thrown in jail together, the brotherhood of the black gang, feared and despised in every port in the world. They were hard-working bastards, the salt of the earth in actual fact. Unfortunately, they were badly paid and badly treated, used like animals. Good workers and fine men, maybe. Nevertheless, the shopkeepers put up their shutters when the coal-burners came to town.

Most of the crew were afraid of the boys down below. Not physical fear — sailors aren't exactly timid creatures — but afraid of getting involved. Tempers frayed and fights broke out at the drop of a sweat rag. It was understandable. I got to know and understand them through my friendship with Matt.

We'd been at sea for about eight days when Pete called me up on deck. 'Look,' he said, 'out there on the starboard beam. Icebergs!'

'Christ! They look like mountains.'

Most of the crew came on deck. Half-naked stokers, bronzed young deck-hands and white-shirted stewards shivered in the salty spray and gazed at the wondrous icebergs off the coast of Newfoundland.

The convoy moved on and broke up, different vessels heading for specific ports. The *Tyndareus* changed course, sailing alone among the breathtaking mountains of shimmering ice, strong sunlight gleaming, dancing, bouncing back into the sky, sparkling diamonds, dazzling beams, a wonderland of brilliant sunlight, ocean swells and silver sheens.

There were two gun crews aboard, one from the Royal Artillery with three gunners and a fat-faced corporal who seemed to be in charge. The other crew were Royal Navy gunners under a petty officer. The army crew broke out some ammunition, loaded the big gun on the after deck and started firing at the icebergs. All hands turned to, crowded the decks and cheered the gunners.

The first officer came topside. 'What the fucking hell do you think you're playing at?' he screamed. 'Cease firing!'

'Gun practice!' roared the corporal, empty shells all round, scorching the mate's snow-white decks and rolling in the scuppers. 'This is the perfect place for gun practice. We haven't fired them during the voyage. I know what I'm doing.'

All guns blazed away, the navy tearing chunks out of the icebergs with a rapid-firing weapon, a crazy-looking monster with rubber shoulder-guards, web harness and silvery shells sticking up like a hedgehog. Missiles flew everywhere with empty shells piling up around the operator's legs and the smell of burning trousers. Giant boulders of ice came crashing into the ocean to the cheers of the lads.

Eventually the *Tyndareus* sailed into Halifax, Nova Scotia. It was nothing special, a shipbuilding community with prohibition, an illicit liquor trade and quite a lot of disrespect for the law.

Apparently, most of the Canadian provinces were dry, though you could obtain booze from the liquor stores. There were no bars, no pubs. This didn't prevent the crew from going ashore and getting drunk. Half of them finished up in jail for fighting in the streets, stealing cars and disorderly conduct. The ship couldn't get up steam without the firemen, so the captain bailed them out.

I wasn't sorry to leave Nova Scotia, a strange place, almost like a movie set for an old-fashioned cowboy picture. Pete and I seemed to spend all our time on tiny ferry boats, speedboats and small motor vessels. It was certainly colourful, with people in bright plaid lumber jackets, lace-up boots and red woollens, but it didn't seem real. I quite expected John Wayne to come strolling down Main Street with an axe on his shoulder and gloves on his hands. That's what I really noticed: all the workmen wore gloves, something quite alien to me.

Captain Fortune also ran a dry ship — no crew bar, no booze, though a well-stocked saloon bar for the passengers and officers. The boys had learned the prohibition tricks, however. When we reached our next port they stocked up with cases of cheap whisky from the stores, got stuck into it during the night and went in search of more. Some went into the bootleg joints and didn't come out again. I supposed we'd see them on sailing day.

Sailing day, however, was a long way off. This was St John, New Brunswick. The longshoremen, stevedores and dockworkers went on strike and refused to unload our ship. Captain Fortune called for volunteers to handle the cargo, man the derricks and load and unload our own vessel. Most of the crew were honorable guys, men who sailed the oceans of the world for a living. They stepped forward and the skipper thought he had solved the problem.

Pete and Butch were among the volunteer dockers but I went ashore to look around and see the sights. When I returned, the quayside was lined with men — real bruisers, broken-nosed and thick-eared with pick handles in their gloved hands. Checkmate, or to use the vernacular of our Canadian cousins, a Mexcian stand-off.

There was violence in the air, and fights occurred every night. Drunks roamed the decks, broke into the ship's store and stole some cases of whisky. Things settled down a bit after that. The firemen stayed in their quarters and drank themselves into a stupor while the rest of the crew enjoyed a well-earned spell ashore. Pete and I hit the town every day, went to the movies, visited the swimming pool and did the natural things that a boy and his best friend would do.

Then fifty French Canadian priets came aboard. They were bound for South America and had mountains of luggage. Some of the dockers returned to work and loading got under way. Pete joined them. The money was extremely good, double pay on Saturday, double-double pay on Sunday and working conditions unknown to Englishmen. Pete was earning a lot of cash and saving it for the next port of call, New York.

The Statue of Liberty, the Hudson river, Brooklyn Bridge, Times Square: New York was exactly as I'd seen it on the movies. Washing hung across the East Side streets, and there were colourful kids and hustlers on every sidewalk. Pete knew what to buy and where to buy. We had a few wonderful nights ashore and then Captain Fortune put a stop to it. That's when the trouble really started.

The boys could get ashore in any other port in the world, but not in New York. The cops carried guns and demanded a landing card with photograph and thumb-print. We moved out a few days later, joined a convoy in the smooth Atlantic and set sail for the Gulf of Mexico.

There had always been a tin of fifty cigarettes on the cabin table. It was the same in every cabin, a ritual closely observed. Things changed when the *Tyndareus* left New York. A carton of 200 American cigarettes appeared on each cabin table. Bottles of rum, vodka and whisky didn't just make an appearance, they showed up in every nook and cranny. There was booze everywhere — in every locker, in with the vegetables, in the refrigeration units, the potato sacks, the apple boxes and stacked under the mountains of coal down below.

The gun crew got stoned out of their minds. I think they were the first to go, probably because they had a rather boring job. Some of the deckhands covered up for the gunners and the ship managed to reach Trinidad. It was beautiful, the old Spanish Main, the pirates' hunting ground — yo-ho-ho and a bottle of booze.

Port of Spain, Tobago, the Caribbean — all the freebooters, buccaneers and sea rovers of my childhood tales came marching from the pages of time to join me on the dirty deck. Pete and I were bunking on deck by this time. Sometimes we made up a couple of sleeping bags in the spud locker.

One fine sunny morning, the first mate woke up to find the ship alone in the South Atlantic. The enormous convoy had sailed on without us, and every man jack in the black gang was blind drunk and dead to the world on the ship's deck. The guys woke up, and started boozing again. Naturally enough, the first mate objected, but backed off when one sozzled fireman threatened to throw him to the sharks. Captain Fortune remained on the bridge, and it was now a case of 'with us or against us'. The deck department — sailors, ordinary seamen and the like — joined in with the black gang for the free booze. The catering staff, and the fifty priests we were transporting, locked themselves in the main saloon and shivered with fright. No one bothered Pete and me, so we stuck to our little nest in the spud locker and enjoyed the performance.

Meanwhile, up on deck, a fight was taking place between Tommy Burns, the toughest broken-headed bully bastard in the whole wide world, and a donkey man who was even tougher. Tommy wanted to turn the ship around, get some steam up and head for some place in South America. The donkey man, stoned out of his cracked skull, wanted to go some place else. It was time for Jamie's forty-five to comfort me. I pinched a soft leather shoulder-harness from a junior officer and carried the gun or kept it very close.

An odd slug of whisky made no difference to Pete and me, but the ship was in danger. Enemy submarines were known to be in the Caribbean but nobody seemed to be doing anything about it. The whole situation got worse as time passed, with drunken brawls and open mutiny. The firemen refused to turn to.

Then the Canadian priests came on deck and held a prayer meeting on the fo'c'sle head. This infuriated the drunks. They belted the priests with lumps of coal and shooed them back to the safety of the saloon. Pete and I thought it was time to choose sides, so we joined our mates in the first-class saloon and awaited further developments.

The skipper must have radioed for assistance because a Brazilian gunboat came on the scene and fired a shot over our bow. The drunks lined the rails and hurled abuse at the strangers before the US Navy came to the rescue and boarded the *Tyndareus*. These were big guys, real professional leg-breakers with huge clubs and machine-guns. They sorted out the worst offenders, arrested them and put them in chains.

Volunteer firemen were called for, but no one answered the call. They didn't have the know-how. The Americans offered to take command and take the ship into port but Captain Fortune wouldn't accept their offer. He left the engineers to scrape together a makeshift team of firemen, and the next morning there was steam in the boilers.

The Yanks cast off and all hands made for the hidden booze. It just went on and on, with the firemen stoned out of their minds. Somehow, we reached South America and dropped off the priests.

The *Tyndareus* moved across the South Atlantic, round the Cape of Good Hope and into Cape Town. The lady in white was there to greet us. She didn't know what she was letting herself in for!

The boys just went crazy. Commando brandy was five shillings a bottle. Starboard Light, a home-brewed concoction of green fire-water, cost only a few coppers per glass, with four bottles for a quid!

It was unbelievable! Some of the crew were jailed, some deserted and some were invited to a wedding. The host, a South African businessman, had made friends with a few of the guys in a bar. He came from England originally, and must have been full of the patriotic bullshit that was flying around the Cape. Whatever the reason, he asked the lads to attend the wedding party at his new home.

Not being gifted with a tremendous amount of foresight, I went along with Pete. We thought it was going to be great fun, plenty of music and some dancing. The guests came in horse-drawn garries, hand-drawn rickshaws and petrol-driven cars. Some arrived on horseback and some on foot — farmers, shopkeepers, nice girls and handsome boys, a good cross-section of the community.

Big Tommy, the terror of the *Tyndareus*, leading moron and biggest villain afloat, arrived in his Sunday best — flat cap and muffler. He looked quite smart, a change from his everyday attire of sweat-rag and dirty vest. Other members of the crew turned up as well: trimmers, firemen, donkey men, all the guys in the black gang. They drank all the booze, ate all the food, screwed all the dames and wrecked the bridegroom's new home.

A couple of firemen were jailed in Cape Town but the skipper replaced them with two bums off the beach, a pair of deserters, winos who could handle a shovel in their sober moments.

The Royal Navy headquarters at Simonstown, the next port of call, were throwing a party, a real banquet. It was one of those very special dinners, all the gleaming silverware on the tables, polished glasses, beautiful linen napkins, plenty of toasts, lots of booze and dozens of boring speeches.

Someone should have warned them.

They invited the crew of the *Tyndareus*. All the boys arrived, polished shoes, clean shirts, well-creased trousers and a few black eyes. It looked like they'd turned over a new leaf but not for long. Big Tommy gave the signal by tipping over the top table. The big shots, naval commanders, admirals, captains of the fleet, sat back in disbelief, fruit salad and fresh cream running down their faces, all mixed up with the gold braid and gleaming decorations. Bright-faced boys in beautiful number ones, the Royal Navy in all its splendour . . . then it really started.

'Let's piss off!' I said to Pete. 'This is the end. We're gonna get killed or thrown in jail. I'm getting out of her.'

'You mean you're quitting? Deserting the *Tyndareus?*'

'Goddam right!' I replied. 'You coming with me?'

'Where can we go?' asked Pete.

'Africa, for Christ's sake. It's a big country!'

'I'll have to think about it,' said Pete. 'What we gonna do for money? How we gonna live? Jesus! It's a big step to take. I might never set foot in Australia again.'

Half the crew were missing when we reached Port Elizabeth, jailed, hospitalised, deserted. I gathered what money I could — a few pounds from Butch, a small advance of pay from the chief steward, and shore-leave money. It didn't amount to much but it was enough for a rail ticket to Durban, three days' journey by train.

Leaving Pete was the worst part. We shed a few tears. He wouldn't leave and I couldn't stay any longer. I packed my grip, slipped away in the middle of the night and caught the early morning rattler, Jamie's forty-five under my shirt, snug and comfy in a spring-loaded holster.

The African veldt opened up before me. It looked good, much more interesting than jumping out of airplanes, far better than sailing the oceans with a load of drunks and bums. Nothing to lose, only my Liverpool accent.

A magnificent African served my lunch on a tray. His skin gleamed and his noble features made him look like a royal prince in servitude. He said he would look after me, make my bunk in the evenings, bring my breakfast in the mornings.

I thought of Pete, Jamie, Jackie Clithero. Why couldn't I settle down with one good guy and be happy? But life kept throwing things at me and I loved every second. I knew something would turn up, nothing spectacular, but just enough to make the adrenalin flow.

Granddad Carter, my mother's father, had been here. He'd fought in the Zulu war, swords and cavalry, spears and shields. I thought about him. Familiar names came to mind, Rorke's Drift, Ladysmith, Bloemfontein, the Spion Cop and the siege of Mafeking. My old man had been there too and the rats had eaten his hair while he slept.

'Come on Africa! Show me what you've got!' I shouted. But there was no one there, no one to hear my cry, just me, all alone in the dark continent.

8. Commando Brandy

When I hit the quiet railway station in Durban, a half-naked Zulu grabbed my bag, shoved it on top of his head and followed me down the platform. 'Do you want a rickshaw?' he asked. The whole day lay ahead of me with no special plans. I gave the guy a coin, dropped the grip in the luggage office and strolled down Pine Street.

A fine-tooth comb and a few pound notes in my kick, I wandered through the marketplace. It looked interesting — tin roofs, a walled surround of red and white brick, witch-doctors at the bones, a kind of fortune-telling ritual. The guy sat on an arse-rubbed rug, cast a few strange-looking bones onto the dusty square and gathered some coins from the excited customers.

Naked Zulu girls paraded the stalls, beautiful young creatures, a band of coloured beadwork slung from the hips, bead anklets, bare breasts, noble faces, baskets of yellow, green and red cane balanced atop their remarkable heads.

Indian traders ran the market stalls, shouted the odds and sold their wares. White people didn't get involved with physical work. It looked like they travelled first class, but where did they find an income? I had to figure that one out. Greeks and Indians drove the cabs, powerful Zulus pulled the rickshaws and ragged kaffirs filled the menial jobs.

Sausage, egg and chips would have been welcome, but there were no cafes. It was a four-course lunch or nothing. I settled for soup, a steak and salad, fresh pineapple and cream, black coffee. The waiters were barefoot blacks in snow-white shorts and half-sleeved tops with bright blue trim. They had two-inch holes in their ear lobes, big rubber-like rings of dangling flesh stretched beyond belief and stuffed with metal discs and painted cotton-reels. They were the only natives who weren't in rags, apart from the rickshaw runners who wore a colourful loincloth and fearsome head-dress.

A fiery sun beat down, so I made my way through the tree-lined streets and found the beach. Perhaps I'd see things clearly after a swim. No dames adorned the gleaming sands. Golden-skinned boys played in the surf, nothing to do but enjoy the day, spend daddy's money on cool ice-creams and ice-cold drinks.

I stripped off my shirt and pants. A ball came my way, so I hitched up my candy-striped under-shorts, tossed the colourful plaything onto muscle beach and joined in the game. The South African lads wore tiny shorts and well-tailored shirts. My clothes were all wrong. I figured I'd have to dress like the locals or be noted by the immigration man.

I needed a room, a furnished apartment in town, some kind of headquarters to work from. There would be a salesman's job, something the native blacks couldn't do. There had to be. Perhaps I'd get lucky.

A kid named Jan tumbled me into the sand. I grabbed a surfboard and moved into the ocean rollers. Jan came after me. Paradise!

The salt stung my eyes. Jan came shooting along on a high roller which knocked me sideways and tore my knickers off. I choked with laughter and swam in the nude, surfboard tied to my wrist. The sandy shorts washed up on the beach and my new acquaintance grabbed them. It was the start of a lovely friendship.

We lay alongside a pile of surfboards. The sun dried my knickers and scorched my skin while Jan teased me about swimming naked. I laughed it off and we moved on to a little horseplay. He pulled my hair. We wrestled. I licked him. He tasted salty and smelled of the sea, and his sing-song accent filled me with pleasure.

English was the popular tongue in Durban but not inland. There they used a variety of Dutch, with a much simplified grammar, called Afrikaans. Everything was written in the two languages. The newspaper was in English so I read it through in the park and found plenty of apartments to rent.

Most of the cheap hotels and furnished rooms were on the Point, a kind of dock road alongside the bay. They weren't quite what I wanted. The North Beach, the other side of the city, was lined with superb hotels and beautiful buildings, a wonderful waterfront more exciting than New York and just as fabulous as Miami. It was far too rich for me. I pencilled a joint on Smith Street and made my way across town. It was getting dark. The bars were closed and there were no women on the streets. Watchmen — canvas-uniformed, peak-capped blacks — squatted in front of the business premises and settled down on the pavement for the long night. Some were armed with clubs and short spears. A few Indian cab drivers roamed the city and searched for fares. The natives vanished quietly from the scene and the brightly lit movie houses spilled their customers onto the spotless pave. A few servicemen crept about and gathered outside the Tops Dance Hall, right opposite the apartment house I sought on Smith Street.

I poked my nose into the foyer of the dance hall, all red plush and sparkling chrome. A young Greek sailor grabbed my wrist. He was very handsome in his, all gold braid and gorgeous uniform, a radio officer in the Greek merchant navy. He spoke English but I couldn't understand a word.

'I don't dance with sailors in public,' I said.

His name was Anton and his laughter was sweet music.

'Starboard light!' he shouted among other things. I figured he wanted a drink. He certainly wanted a boy.

'The bars closed at six!' I shouted but he hung on to my arm and wanted to make friends as I strolled across to Marrling Mansions. A uniformed porter met me at the desk. 'I want a room for a week,' I said. 'My bags are at the railway station but I'd like to move in tonight.' He gave me a key and showed me to a suite of rooms on the first floor. It was excellent, a superb service flat with kitchen, lounge, bathroom, shower and twin-bedded room.

Communication with Anton was impossible: I couldn't understand a word and he couldn't stop laughing. We crossed town, hit the main stem and found a dazzling hotel on West Street. A night on the bottle was the last thing I wanted but I couldn't resist the young Greek's happy smile and the drinks were cheap.

Anton had a few too many Starboard lights and was in no condition to go roaming the docks in search of his ship. We ordered a tray of black coffee and he laced it with fresh cream and brandy. First class all the way! No bars for the bums and servicemen but superb hotel service if you knew where to find it. I tried to get him into a cab but he hung on to me and seemed to know what he wanted. Arm in arm, we made our unsteady way across the city and wandered into Marrling Mansions.

A kaffir 'boy' and 'girl' went with the apartment. The lad looked after the rooms and the girl did the laundry and kitchen work. Jed was waiting for us, a good-looking Zulu lad, lovely teeth and shiny skin. He took us up in the lift, showed us into the flat and offered to make some coffee.

Anton tried to kiss me. I slipped his hold, went into the bedroom and took my clothes off. He came after me.

'I'm going to take a shower,' I said. 'Take your pants off and join me.'

He was out like a light when I got back, so I undressed him, hung his smart-looking uniform in a wardrobe and tucked him into his bed. He was still asleep when I awoke so I took a rickshaw to the station and collected my bag.

After breakfast I hit West Street and bought some tiny shorts and colourful button-down short-sleeved shirts. Long knee-length stockings and leather boscos on my feet completed the transformation. I looked like any other young South African: brown as hell and bright as a button . . .

Anton stayed with me for a few days, and the games he wanted to play in bed — well, I guess the Greeks had a word for it! He was a nice enough guy but verbal communication was a bit awkward. Anyway, I gave him a hug at the dockside, and he sailed away on the Heraklion.

A Greek woman ran the apartment house. The staff called her the Missus. I dropped into her office to settle my account for the week.

'Your friend paid a month's rent in advance,' she said. 'Are you going to be with us for some time?'

'Yes,' I replied. 'I'm settling down in Durban.'

'I think you'll be comfortable here,' said the Missus.

Things improved rapidly. The African lad came in to make the beds and tidy up the apartment. His eyes lit up when he saw a bottle of Commando brandy on the sideboard. 'Hey boss,' he said, 'that's real good stuff!'

'Help yourself,' I said. 'There are plenty of glasses. I'm going to take a shower.'

I had six or seven pounds in my pocket but no real plans. I thought of heading down to the docks and making enquiries at the Seamen's Mission. Someone there would know the ropes.

Jed came in with a towel. 'Did you have a snort of brandy?' I enquired. He wrapped the thick cotton towelling round me. His thin shorts bulged when he helped me dress. I liked his searching eyes and gentle touch.

He hadn't touched the bottle. 'Did you change your mind?' I asked. Jed helped me into a fresh shirt. I offered him the brandy. 'I'll give you one pound for the bottle,' he said.

'I don't want your money,' I answered. 'Take the bottle. It only cost five shillings and I didn't buy it.'

'You buy five bottles and I pay you five pounds,' replied the lad. 'Very good business, boss.'

'Tell me more,' I said.

There was something special between us. Jed knew I grew excited beneath his touch. He explained the drink situation: only whites could purchase liquor. There were native bars in the poor quarters but they only sold mealy-meal drinks, a kind of substitute beer with little or no alcohol content.

Half a dozen bottles put me in business and it progressed from there. Jed found a small market among his fellow-workers in the city and built up a little bootleg round. A week's expense money satisfied me at first but I still searched for a more reliable way of earning a living. Then Jed introduced me to a rickshaw runner, a ferocious young man with a body like a lion and a fearsome head-dress — buffalo horns, tiger skin and human bones. His name was Timbo and he had many friends in the native compounds, Zulu homesteads and kraals outside the city limits.

A liquor squad operated in Durban, Natal, and probably throughout South Africa. Their job was the control of liquor, and the squad worked in conjunction with the police authority. All liquor consignments had to be accounted for, signed for and entered in a book kept by the retailer. These books were examined monthly and the squad checked up any extra large orders or what appeared to be excess consumption.

This disturbed me in the early stages of our operation and caused me to travel round the different liquor stores leaving a trail of false names. An address wasn't necessary unless the goods were to be delivered. Now, however, we worked hand in glove with a Greek storekeeper, only too glad of the extra business we put his way. He solved the problem with a stroke of his pen; all the booze was allocated, on paper that is, to ships in the harbour, many of which had already sailed.

We rented a garage from him and used it as a storehouse, kept our stock under lock and key, even guarded by a uniformed kaffir. The boy actually sat outside our garage all through the night. This was customary; every shop doorway had a squatting Zulu and some carried assegai and knobkerrie. I often wondered about the armed guards. Even the black police officers had no power to hold or detain a white person, and it seemed ridiculous.

Business was running smoothly and it didn't cost much to live even in our luxurious suite. Unfortunately, it took a long time for a kaffir boy to save a pound and indeed some would never own a pound note in the whole of their life.

The big sales lay with the chiefs, who ran the 'shebeens' — shanty houses, whorehouses, and joints where a guy could get a drink when the bars closed, along with a dose of pox . . . Guys of all creeds and colours visited the shebeens, but we had not tapped that market as yet, as it was way out of town.

Chiefs and headmen bought the liquor and sold it in the shebeens and illicit drinking dens. There were others involved in the bootleg brandy racket. They diluted the potent fire-water, tampered with the labels and charged enormous prices.

I allowed Jed and Timbo to advise me. Consequently we built up a good reputation and I felt reasonably safe. A few guys tried to hijack me, but one look down the barrel of a forty-five changed their minds.

Two days' work produced enough cash for a week's expenses and entertainment. I wasn't greedy, and enjoyed the golden beach by day and the fabulous cinemas by night. Durban cinemas had to be seen to be believed. They were magnificent, wondrous decor and breathtaking art. The Bioscope was my favorite house of entertainment, a small but very attractive picture palace near Smith Street. Not one of the big city movie houses, the Bioscope offered pots of tea and snacks to every customer. This was included in the ticket price and served at small side tables next to each seat. I'm sure the Bioscope was the only theatre in Durban where whites and non-Europeans mixed, though unfortunately even this didn't extend to the native Zulu and kaffir.

Some of my evenings were spent in the Tops Dance Hall. It was only fifty paces from where I lived, a lively joint full of colourful young people and girls who danced for the price of a threepenny ticket. They called them taxi dancers. If a guy wanted a partner, he had to purchase tickets and the young hostess was obliged to dance with him while his tickets lasted.

Two young Americans became friendly with me in the Tops, Sam and his partner Buddy. They were seafaring lads, pleasant youngsters enjoying a night on the town. Buddy wanted a drink and Sam wasn't quite sure what he wanted.

The bars close early in Durban, and I mean real early, like six or seven in the evening. Even then they only cater for drunken sailors and poor whites. If you really want a decent drink in comfortable surroundings, then you need to use a hotel.

'Holy cow!' said Buddy as we strolled outside at midnight. 'I could use some of that Cape Smoke right now.'

'I've got some brandy and a few bottles of Coke in the house,' I said. 'You're welcome to a snort.'

They accepted without a moment's hesitation, and we all traipsed up to the apartment. Music from a small collection of records passed a pleasant hour away. Sam talked about the war at sea and Buddy drank like a fish. It was two o'clock in the morning when Buddy seemed to crumple. His engaging smile vanished, the gleam went out of his eye, his mouth opened and his head fell back.

'He's out!' cried Sam. 'Holy Christ! What am I gonna do with him?'

'Shove him in bed,' I suggested.

'Here?'

'Why not? You can't leave him like that. Take his shoes off.'

Buddy came to in the bedroom. 'Goddam!' he mumbled.

Sam pulled the lad's pants off, bundled him into bed, dragged the covers over his long lean body.

'He'll be alright in the morning,' I said.

'Thanks,' Sam replied. 'This is a neat joint. You gotta partner?'

'No,' I answered. 'I'm by myself.'

'Looks like a joint for two,' replied the young American.

'Well it ain't,' I said. 'It's a big apartment and I guess it looks better with two beds. You want some coffee?'

'Lead me to it,' Sam said. 'Make it black and make it sweet. You know somepin'? You're the first English guy I met.'

The night was cool and an ocean breeze drifted in from the bay. Red and green neon lights from the dance hall flashed and reflected in the comfortable living-room. I put my empty coffee cup down. 'The bathroom is through there,' I reminded him. 'You'll find everything you want. Help yourself to a robe, pyjamas, whatever you need. Look in the hot cupboard. Make yourself at home. I'm dead.'

I liked guys like Buddy and Sam. There was something fresh and charming about them, a gentle sort of innocence. I hoped they cared for one another and wondered what the relationship was. Maybe nothing, just bunkies, cabin mates on the town.

Sam was an attractive boy, shiny brown chest and spotless knickers, he padded barefoot to his sleeping friend, pulled back the cover and sat on the edge of the cot. 'Hell!' he said. 'You ever sleep with a drunk?'

I laughed. 'What's wrong?'

'Every goddam thing! He's dead to the world and I can't shift him.'

'Let him be,' I said. 'Bunk in with me. There's plenty of room.'

Two or three inches separated our hot skins. I felt the heat from his shoulders on my back. He turned. We weren't restless, just trying to adjust. Bare legs came together, faces close and cheeks almost touching. Sam stretched out his legs. 'Sorry,' he said. 'Did I disturb you?'

I made a sleepy sound and put a hand on his hip. Other movements drew us closer and the bare dicks rubbed together. Sam gripped them, played them up and down. My face nestled into his lovely cheeks and fragrant hair. His arms went round me and the escaping fluids ran over our skin.

'I'm sorry,' he whispered.

'Don't worry about it,' I replied. 'It was my fault. I got too horny.'

'And me,' said the lad. 'I got excited. I guess it's because I never slept with anyone before.'

That should have been the end of it. The boys returned to their ship at noon and I spent the rest of the day on the beach with Jan and the local guys. Sam called late in the evening. Jed brought him up in the lift and asked if we wanted coffee.

It's alright,' I replied. 'I'll make the coffee. My friend's staying the night. You can get away, Jed.'

'No trouble, boss,' the Zulu lad replied. He moved into the kitchen and we heard him chanting as he cleared up.

'I went to the movies with Buddy,' Sam said. 'He's gone back to the ship. I wanted to see you again, so, what the hell! I'm here, ain't I?'

Sam stayed for a couple of days, long enough to fall in love with Africa, meet my friends on the beach and enjoy the thrills and spills of the ocean rollers.

'I'm gonna jump ship,' he said. 'She can sail without me.'

'Don't be foolish,' I said. 'You'll find yourself in a load of trouble. You'll miss your friends and you'll get homesick. Think it over, Sam.'

He was a very innocent boy. He couldn't discuss sex and I was afraid of embarrassing him. Boys like Sam might think of other lads, sleep with them and play with them in bed but couldn't possibly talk about such things. Even when he admitted jerking off with his high-school buddy, I wasn't quite sure what he was saying. Our bedtime romps had not moved out of the first stages of boyhood bliss but his friendly kisses told me everything. He was a homosexual boy and something was bound to happen. Sexually, we were very immature and easily satisfied.

We could have been in love and we certainly needed each other, so when he missed his ship, I joined him on the Point and we waved goodbye together.

'That's it!' Sam said. 'Now we can get some American know-how in this goddam racket of yours.'

Business became more interesting and much more profitable, an excursion into the unknown — the Valley of a Thousand Hills, Zululand and all its magic people. They were so very regal, majestic and beautiful, and I was so very young and ignorant.

'They're off!' The familiar sound filled the air at Durban racetrack. The excited spectators seethed to the post and rail fence to witness the thunder of hooves, galloping steeds, colourful silks and snow-white britches. Rich green turf, bright blue skies, a pink flamingo overhead completed a glorious afternoon in the sun.

The stands were filled with well-dressed sportsmen, beautiful ladies in all their summer splendour, runners and bookies at the rail. Crowds of kaffirs and Zulus moved about in a separate enclosure outside the track.

A young white boy sat cross-legged on the grass. He wore a pair of thin white trousers and had calf-length snake boots on his feet. Bare-chested and brown from the sun, golden-haired and blue-eyed, he fascinated me.

'Hey, Sam,' I said, 'place the bets. I'm going to see what's happening outside. See you later.'

The boy had a crown-and-anchor board at his feet and a crowd of untidy native lads around him. The kaffirs gambled on his board, a dice game, very simple but all the odds in the banker's corner. A punter won at every throw of the dice, but many lost and the boy raked in the cash.

His control was wonderful and he seemed to be conversant in Bantu, Hindi, and all the noisy tongues around his gaming-board. He smiled when I approached and made a wager. 'You're on the wrong side of the track,' he said.

'It doesn't bother me,' I replied. 'How's your luck?'

'I make a living,' said the lad. 'Come on! Get your money down! You come here in rags and go away in fucking motor-cars!'

The game progressed and I made a little headway.

'Listen,' I said. 'I'm with a friend. Can we meet when this is over? I'd like to talk to you.'

He pointed to his battered suitcase. 'That's my home,' he said. 'You'll find me here every day. I'm staying till the meeting's finished. This is my office. I follow the crowds.'

'I have to go,' I explained. 'My friend will wonder where I am. Don't bugger off. I'd love to see you again.'

The lad got on with his business and I went back to the stands.

'What happened to you?' asked Sam. 'I've been looking all over the track. Where the hell you been?'

I explained about the boy, said I wanted to meet him later, take him for a meal and invite him home.

'For Christ's sake!' Sam said. 'You don't know him. He's a goddam racetrack tout, a no-good bum. What's wrong with you?'

'You'll change your mind when you see him,' I replied. 'Believe me, Sam. This kid's got everything. We need a guy like him in our operation. He speaks the lingo and handles the blacks like children.'

'If you wanna make friends with the guy,' Sam said quietly, 'that's ok by me but don't mention business.'

We found him packing his bag.

'Hi!' I said. 'Remember me? This is my buddy, Sam. There's a cab waiting for us. We had a couple of winners. How about joining us for a meal?'

'What's the catch?' asked the boy. 'What do you want from me?'

'Nothing. No strings attached. You seem to be by yourself, and I want to make friends. What's so strange about that?'

'He's a Yank, you're English and I'm an Afrikaner,' said the lad. 'What's on your mind, some kind of business proposition? I'm all ears.'

'Let's have dinner and get to know each other,' I suggested. 'What have you got to lose?'

The evening began with steak and wine and friendly conversation. The boy's name was Matt, a wanderer who travelled all over Africa. Wherever there was a circus, a fair or a travelling show, you'd find a boy like Matt, survivors living from hand to mouth, but roaming free and wild. He made my mouth water.

The wine made us mellow, tongues ran loose at the lip.

'Throw in with me and Sam,' I said. 'Give it a try. You can earn a living with us.'

'I'll think about it,' Matt replied.

'We've got a decent apartment in town,' I said. 'Stay for a couple of days and get to know us. There's plenty of room.'

Sam went to the washroom, and the waiter prepared the bill.

'You were too generous with the tip,' Matt remarked. 'That's foolish. Money doesn't grow on trees.'

'It's my lucky day, Matt. You gonna stay the night?'

Matt smiled. We picked up Sam in the men's room and made our way across town.

A free rover, Matt wasn't particular where he spent his nights. He slept in stable yards, shared the hospitality of circus hands, dossed down in caravans and, if he had enough cash at the time, rented a room in a small hotel.

'Don't you get tired of drifting?' I asked, spooning sugar into his coffee and trying to make him feel welcome.

Matt relaxed in the easy chair. 'Never thought about it,' he said. 'Too busy earning a living and keeping out of trouble. It's okay when I'm with a big outfit. I was fourteen when I joined a stunt motor circus. It was terrific! I used to change out of my school uniform, do a day's work and go home with a pocket full of cash. My stepfather knew nothing about it and we didn't get along, so when the circus moved on I went with them. I've been on the loose ever since.'

'Sounds exciting,' remarked Sam. 'Jesus! I'd love to travel with a road show.'

'It can get lonely,' Matt replied, 'but you hear the drone of the dynamo, the generators going all the time, the music and the screams. It gets in your blood. There's a smell of candy-floss and popcorn, free rides on the dodgem, the big wheel, depends on the outfit you're with.'

'How about friends?' I enquired. 'Sounds like an ideal way of life if you have a good partner.'

'I made a few pals along the way,' explained the boy. 'No one special. Most of the hands are black. I was with a European fair, big guys, all muscle and tattoos, but when they got you in their sleeping bag, all they wanted was plenty of poke.'

He pulled a poster from his bag. 'What do you think of that?' he said. 'That's me on the wall of death.' It was a picture of Matt sitting on the handlebars of an Indian, a special kind of stunt motorbike.

'The driver is Crash Cavanagh, a Hollywood stunt merchant who crashed cars for a living,' explained the boy. 'Sometimes he carried a lion on the handlebars.'

Sam was quite impressed. 'Why the hell did you leave a set-up like that?' he asked.

'I didn't leave,' said the lad. 'The war with Japan broke out and most of the Americans went back to the States. Anyway, I like being on my own. There's always something interesting, a horse show, a race meeting. I can get by wherever I am.'

Sam took a shower and returned to the living-room with a towel around his waist. 'You guys will talk all night,' he said. 'I'm gonna hit the sack. So long, see ya in the morning.'

Matt scraped a finger through his scalp. 'Head's itchy,' he observed. 'My hair needs washing.'

I offered to make up a bed on the settee. Matt rubbed his head vigorously. 'Don't bother,' he said. 'Let's take a shower. I can bunk in with you or Sam.'

He fished a clean pair of knickers from his bag.

'Sling your gear in the laundry basket,' I suggested. 'It'll be washed and pressed before you wake up.'

Matt was a rare beauty, smooth as silk from head to toe. Fresh as a daisy, a fine down covered his upper lip. One testicle was missing but he was sheer perfection in spite of the absent part. Sweet little curls peeped from beneath his arms, corn-coloured and shiny. His stomach was flat and his waist was trim. The hair about his pubic region was copper-coloured and clung to his firm young belly like paint.

Water cascaded over our nakedness. It was cool and delicious, the perfect way to end the day. Matt's bottom was not quite dry when he climbed into his shorts. They clung to his skin, tight and damp and full of beautiful boy. He tossed back his head, pulled a face in the mirror, opened his mouth and blinked his eyes.

'I feel great after that,' he said. 'Lead the way. I'm not getting out of bed till dinner time.'

His warmth and fragrance came to me beneath the sheets. One hand on his neat waist, the seat of his damp little knickers touched me and set everything in motion. I kissed his skin and felt him stiffen beneath my touch. Kissing a boy's bare hide is sheer magic and my lips moved as light as a feather. He peeled back the waistband of his shorts and felt the softness of my touch. A tiny bite made him jump.

Matt came face to face, our mouths pressed lightly and sexual parts pressed hard together when we kissed.

'You smell like a dream!' I sighed.

Matt put his mouth to my ear. 'You doused me with something,' he giggled.

'Only shampoo.'

He sniffed at my skin. 'Mmmm!' he murmured. 'I like guys who kiss. Most fellers only want a bit of poke.'

His hot bare flesh flattened onto me. We exchanged kisses and rolled about with pleasure. His single testicle moved in my palm, and I fondled it lovingly. 'You're very beautiful,' I sighed.

Matthew pressed his mouth to the front of my shorts. 'Take 'em off,' he whispered. 'I want to kiss all over.'

Loving just came natural and kept us busy all through the night.

Threesomes played an important role in my life and always had, so I wasn't surprised when Sam and Matt fell in love and Matt joined our illegal operations. He was no newcomer to the brandy game and had played it many times before. Something made me ask him to think again, but he knew what he was getting into.

'Forget about it,' he said. 'I can look after myself.'

The Missus accepted our new friend and offered us a much larger apartment on the next floor, but we decided to stay put and received an extra bed from the stores, a foldaway that remained folded away.

Sam really lost his heart to young Matt. I wasn't sorry. The dreamy look in their eyes gave me the utmost pleasure, and left me free to follow my natural quest: the pursuit of boys.

The rickshaw boys fascinated me. They came from every age group, magnificent specimens, lissom and muscular, wonderful frames aglow. They washed beneath a tap in the hiring yard, donned a loincloth, adjusted a fearsome head-dress, paid a few coppers to the hire boss and rented a cart for the day.

Indians and Asians chewed on the betel nut, a kind of peppercorn rolled in a leaf of kif, mowie-wowie or simple pepper leaf. They spat the sticky red juice into the wind and reached a high.

Rickshaw runners didn't need any stimulant. They ran for miles, muscles rippling in the sun, strong bare feet pounding the roads and waterfront streets, big smiles, eyes aglow, fat Europeans sitting comfortably in the two-wheeled carriage.

There was so much beauty all around, but the comely boys of Durban eclipsed all — matchless, breathtaking beauties, second to none. I found them on the sidewalks, in the parks and at the movies, sparkling lads, splendid youths and blooming young boys.

An open shirt, the flash of golden skin, a glimpse of bare back and narrow waist beneath a rumpled garment, copper-coloured legs and muscular bottoms, there were so many! The prowl, the hunt and the exciting chase makes the heart pound. No secret handshake, no old school tie, no badge — only a knowing wink, the flutter of an eyelash, the raised brow. The touch of a friendly fingertip makes the hand tremble and the knee shake, and a boy's submissive kiss can strike you dumb!

Boy-watching led me to the beach at night and it was there that I met a lad named Nicky, one of Jan's young set. The kids lit fires, played a little music and swam in the nude after dark. A few girls joined in, cousins and sisters, lovely boys and girls from the best side of town.

Nicky's astonishing beauty sent me in chase. I couldn't stop admiring him. He was refreshing, alluring, a pleasure-giving boy, seductive and charming. I knew instinctively that he liked me but we hadn't reached the stage where one could invite the other to his home for a visit or to spend the night.

Matt and Sam joined in the midnight bathing sessions. Matt was the only one who didn't swim naked. Nicky questioned me about the lad. He knew we shared the same apartment. 'What's wrong with Matt?' he asked. 'He always keeps his pants on.'

'How would I know?' I replied. 'He's just shy, I guess. We don't all have fabulous bodies like you. Some guys are just ordinary.'

Nicky pulled a damp towel over his lower half. 'Matt is no ordinary looking guy,' he said. 'I wish he was my friend and shared a flat with me. I like him very much. Does he sleep in the same room as you?'

I slipped away from the glow of the fire and ran into the water. Nicky came after me. Our bodies touched beneath the salty waves and we felt the sexual flow between us.

'What's up?' asked the boy.

The moonlight glanced from his lovely face, his smooth-skinned cheeks, his curved young breast. Salt spray ran into his open mouth, streamed from his hair and down his shoulders. He pulled me under. We clung together and let the tremendous sensations free.

'Matthew is Sam's friend,' I gasped. 'Why don't you call around some evening? You can spend a weekened with us if you want.'

Nicky stood up at the water's edge and faced the rolling surf. He was very excited, beautiful penis stiff as a poker. Our bare skin touched, smooth and wet and shining in the moonlight.

'We can't go back like this,' he said. 'Let's go out as far as we can and let the rollers bring us in.'

Pietermaritzburg was a short journey by rail, a small country town in Natal. Nicky asked me to spend the day there. During the course of the evening we were arrested by the patrol, a semi-military or special branch of the South African police force.

'We haven't done anything wrong!' Nicky protested. 'We've only been shopping.'

The cop shoved us into a cell. 'You can complain in the morning,' he shouted. 'The lights will go out in a couple of minutes. Shut up and get ready for bed!'

'I want to telephone my father!' cried Nicky.

Another cop came along. He carried a whip made of rhino hide, a fearful-looking weapon. 'Are we going to have trouble?' he asked quietly.

'No,' answered Nicky. 'Can we have another blanket? There's only one bed.'

'This is a police station,' said the cop with the whip, 'not a hotel. Now go to bed, sonny!' He slammed the cell door and the lights went out.

I had never been in jail before but the situation didn't really disturb me. We made up a pillow with our clothes, cuddled beneath the solitary blanket and held each other close.

Nicky was scared. 'I hope they don't keep us here forever,' he moaned.

'There must be some explanation,' I said soothingly. 'Let's get some sleep. We'll find out in the morning.'

It was an enormous bed, a wooden structure capable of sleeping four or five, and situated in the centre of the cell floor. There were no washing or toilet facilities, nothing, just four whitewashed walls.

My friend's hand crept into my shorts and stroked my bare bottom. His lovely cheeks had never known the feel of a razor. I touched his face with my lips, pulled his knickers down, felt him carefully, gently.

'When we get out of here,' said Nicky, 'will you come home with me? You'll like my family. Mom and Dad will make you welcome, and you know my sister. She's nice.'

'She's not as nice as you,' I whispered. I wet his bottom with saliva.

'Not here,' said Nicky. 'We've got enough problems. Wait until we get home.'

'We might not get an opportunity like this,' I said. 'I want to make love to you, Nicky. I want to put it up your bottom.'

Nicky held me close. 'I've got a much better bed than this,' he whispered. 'You can share it with me. It's alright. I often bring my friend home for the weekend, and we always sleep together.'

There was a disturbance in the corridor, a lot of noisy voices, the sound of chains clanking. Nicky sat up, clung to my hand. 'Blacks!' he moaned. 'Jesus Christ! I hope they don't throw them in with us!'

Dawn sneaked through the prison bars, a glorious day of sunshine, freedom. The cell door opened with a crash.

'You can go,' said the duty officer. No apologies. We climbed into our pants, washed in cold water and flew to the railway station, shirts in hand. Apparently we'd been mistaken for two young army deserters who'd been picked up in the night. Case closed. Run like hell! Only a fool argues with the South African police. A person could be arrested and kept in custody for an indeterminate period. Nicky wouldn't even tell his family about the incident in case his father kicked up a fuss and found himself in deep trouble.

There were many good reasons for staying on in Durban, mostly young and beautiful. However, I felt a longing for the sea, and yet, it wasn't exactly the sea, it was the unknown. There was something out there for me. Out where? I didn't really know but I had to get there. Life was calling again and I didn't want to miss anything.

Mitchell Cotts, a worldwide shipping agency, had an office in the city. They acted for the Blue Funnel Company. I called and told them I'd deserted the *Tyndareus*.

'Will you give evidence against the mutineers?' asked the office manager. 'The enquiry takes place at the Shipping Federation in Liverpool.'

'I don't mind answering questions,' I replied.

'Good,' said the agent. 'We'll ship you back to England as soon as possible.'

I said goodbye to my friends and moved into a hotel, care of Mitchell Cotts. Two days went by, then a black cop called and told me I was under arrest. I packed my grip and followed the cop to a parked car. A white cop drove me to an internment camp on the edge of town, a great wooden stockade patrolled by black guards in ill-fitted uniforms, peaked caps askew, seven-foot spears in hand, bare feet, open fly. Twists of chewing tobacco hung from the earlobes.

A bunch of guys were pitching horseshoes in the compound, an American country boy's game strictly for the peasants. A steel spike was driven into the dirt and guys threw horseshoes at it from about twenty paces: score one for an outer, two for an inner and three for a ringer. Easy enough if you could count to three.

One of the players approached me. 'Hi!' he said. 'The name's Putt Mottman. I'm an American. Let me introduce you to the gang.'

The guys were great, a colourful bunch of undesirable aliens from every place on earth. Some were political prisoners, all had nothing to do but laze around and pitch horseshoes. The food was quite good, and the sleeping quarters were not unlike those of any modern army — wooden huts, two-tier bunks and clean bedding.

An amazing collection of coins passed among the inmates. They used them for gambling, thousands of them — nickels, dimes, florins, liras, pesetas, francs, drachmas and threepenny joeys. God knows where they came from but they never left the camp. The boys played poker every night and the coins changed hands continually, all the players quite conversant with the world rates of exchange and not caring a toss if they lost a rouble and won half-a-crown. All the low cards were removed from the poker decks and some exciting hands came up.

Mottman seemed to be the unofficial camp leader, very self-assured and confident. He created publicity stunts for American firms. He'd been lost in the Amazon, reported missing in central Africa, driven a motorbike around the world. He was billed as the world champion wrestler, world's number one stunt motorcyclist, and international champion horseshoe putter, hence the name Putt Mottman. In the great days of American ballyhoo and publicity Putt had been one of the most daring performers, and the dreadful scars on his body were part of his reward. His scrapbook was full of the most outrageous clippings and publicity cuttings.

Putt himself, however, was quite an unassuming character, friendly and willing to do almost anything for his fellow creatures, regardless of a huge poster above his bed: Putt Mottman, The Strongest Man In The World! All the prisoners went to him with their troubles. I didn't have any special problem but I had six bottles of brandy and a loaded forty-five in my bag.

'What the hell am I gonna do with this little lot?' I asked.

'Drink the goddam stuff,' advised Putt. 'Let's have a party. You ain't thinking of crashing out of this joint are you?'

'No,' I said. 'I wouldn't dream of it.'

'Well, don't,' replied Putt. 'The guards will spear you, and they never miss. Keep the shooting iron locked away. Nobody's gonna search you now.'

Six bottles seemed a reasonable amount to start the party off. There were a dozen guys in the hut I shared, and as the night progressed others joined in. Bottles of wine appeared, Greek boys danced arm in arm and individuals produced their particular party piece. Among them was a Hong Kong lad named Steven, a coffee-coloured youth with the face of an angel, shiny black hair and skin like a girl.

He must have been of mixed blood; no single ethnic origin could have produced such rare beauty. Steven spoke several languages. He'd been shipwrecked and put ashore in Laurenco Marques, Portuguese East Africa, a neutral country. Consequently, he'd mixed with German survivors, Italian deserters and all kinds of aliens trapped in the neutral zone. After a while, he'd made his way across the border and reached Natal, but because he had no papers and no means of identity, they'd thrown him in the camp with the South African aliens.

Steven usually dressed in a sarong, a kind of tartan skirt, quite common in Durban but mostly worn by Malays and Javanese seafarers. All the camp inmates went bare-chested. It saved laundry, and upper garments were not desirable in the heat of the enclosed compound.

Someone produced a bowl of home-made rice wine, a bottle of pure cane spirit and a bucket of camp jungle juice — a raisin and grape concoction produced in the cook-house. Naturally enough, everybody settled down on anybody's bunk and got stoned out of their skulls. When I awoke the birds were singing, gorgeous Steven was in my bunk and we both had lovely erections.

'What happened?' I said.

Steven smiled at me. 'Nothing happened,' he said. 'We just slept in your bunk. I went out like a light but you went first. Did you enjoy the party?'

'I'm not quite sure,' I replied, 'but I would have enjoyed it a lot better if I hadn't drunk that fire water. Let's clean up for breakfast. I'm hungry.'

Steven threw his cotton skirt on my bunk and we went to the washrooms.

Having an attractive friend makes the days pass easy. Steven and I enjoyed each other's company and I waited patiently for another party. You couldn't just jump into a friend's bunk in the night. It wasn't done. The guys would have thought it most peculiar.

Eventually, above the chanting of the kaffir chain-gangs — the black convicts who worked on the docks — I heard the friendly voice of freedom.

'You're going home on the *Orontes*,' said the immigration man. 'Mitchell Cotts have booked your passage.'

He shook hands with me at the gangway and saw me aboard. Most of the Europeans were being shipped to England. Their own countries were occupied by German and Italian armies. Unfortunately, the Americans had to wait for a Stateside vessel. Steven claimed dual nationality, Hong Kong and British. He was shipped back as a DBS, distressed British subject, a miserable way to treat a shipwreck survivor. He had no cash and no means of getting any until he found a job or secured another berth on a ship.

Different countries treated their subjects in different ways, but the chief steward of the *Orontes* simply bundled them all into second-class cabins and treated them with equal fairness. Steven and I were probably the youngest pair of undesirables, and managed to secure a cabin for two.

The deck felt good beneath my feet. The *Orontes* was one of the finest passenger liners afloat and, although she was being used for transporting troops, still managed to produce five-course lunches and seven-course dinners in both first- and second-class saloons. Clean shirts and trousers were acceptable dress in the dining saloons, but anywhere else aboard the vessel you could dress as you pleased. This meant absolutely nothing beneath a cool sheet, and a pair of shorts or swimming garment on deck.

The Mediterranean was now open and an American task force was fighting on the shores of North Africa, so the *Orontes* sailed through the straits of Madagascar, headed for the Red sea and a short cut to the action by way of the Suez canal. Through the gates of hell we sailed, two fantastic rocks at the Red sea entrance, with the Royal Air Force overhead and German submarines down below. On we sailed into the Suez canal. Donkey boys and camel herders pulled down their pantaloons or raised their cotton burnous. Arabs liked to wave their only possessions in the air, give the Europeans a treat. Every native on the banks of the Suez flashed a long limp penis and a hefty pair of testicles. It must have been the national salute.

Alexandria loomed up on the starboard bow. It had been the chief port in Egypt 300 years before Christ came on the scene. Alexander the Great had asked the citizens to keep the place clean, but they hadn't taken any notice. Horse shit from the Roman legions still clung to the stinking streets and foul alleyways. Bubonic plague, the black death, was raging in the city. Rats walked along the sidewalks and open drains. Pimps sold glossy pictures of women being screwed by donkeys and tried to flog small packets of Spanish fly, an aphrodisiac made from dead and diseased bugs. Passengers and crew who wished to go ashore had to have an injection and a medical examination on return. Egypt: the arsehole of the universe.

Steven and I went ashore and got stoned senseless on a hubbly-bubbly pipe. Every cafe had a bunch of these pipes on the tables. I'm not sure what was in them, but I think it was hashish.

Gorgeous crescent-moon flags fluttered in the breeze. People wore a colourful red fez, a filthy striped ankle-length shirt and nothing else. It was a pest hole. Syphilis and gonorrhoea ran unchecked. US Army notices were displayed at regular intervals: Danger! Off Limits! Venereal Disease! You Have Been Warned!

At the quayside, filthy half-naked human beings toiled up and down the gangways day and night. Sacks of coal on their brown backs, they loaded the ships with fuel, thousands of human escalators, turban heads and bare arses. Nothing had changed since the beginning of time. Everything was done by hand. Overseers screamed and cursed. The human ants toiled on. Was this how they built the pyramids, constructed the sphinx, created Pharos lighthouse, the wonders of the world? Meanwhile young boys were bought and sold, castrated and put on the market again. Man was capable of anything.

A few troops came aboard, not exactly hospital cases but guys on their way home. Some had limbs missing. Jacky Nolan was among them, one of my first childhood friends. He'd lost a leg. We'd shared some intimate schoolboy moments in his home above the comic shop in Everton Road. It made me sad. I liked Jacky Nolan, so I avoided him because he made me feel uncomfortable.

Sailing through the Mediterranean was a continuous battle, a gauntlet run of aircraft, bombs, and chattering machine-gun fire. The main event a glorious movie in technicolour, no charge for a seat in the front stalls! Sunken ships in the harbours, torpedoes in the night, the capture of Sardinia, the invasion of Sicily. It was all happening!

A heavy sea sent us rolling, a long slow one, a real stomach-churner. It sent me sliding along the slippery deck of the shower. I pulled a pair of knickers on, walked into the cabin and found Steven on my bunk. He wore a silky sarong about his waist, his regular sleeping outfit. He looked at me, eyes brown and beautiful. 'I hope we reach England in one piece,' he said.

I sat beside him, put an arm across his smooth-skinned shoulder, smelt his fragrance, his sweet breath, his body chemicals, his shiny black hair. What a gorgeous boy!

'Not far to go,' I said, 'only a few more days.'

'I wonder what they'll do with me,' he said. 'My grandfather is English but I'm not. I've never been there. Is it really cold and damp?'

His nearness made me aroused. We'd never been so close since the night of the party, but when I leaned back on the pillow Steven sat up. 'Do you want to get in your bunk?'

'Not yet,' I replied. 'Stay with me and talk.'

He reached up and adjusted the air vent above our heads. I took his arm and pulled him down beside me.

'What are you doing?' he giggled, lips parted, soft hair across his forehead, brown cheeks flushing scarlet.

'Just getting comfortable.'

Our heads came together on the pillow. His hair touched my cheek and I pulled a sheet over us.

'We mustn't sleep together,' he said softly. 'I can't move. There's not much room and I don't know what to do with my left arm.'

My hand slid beneath his sarong and rested on a well-filled pair of knickers.

'Don't!' he said. 'We mustn't . . . you shouldn't . . .'

'I only touched you. Put your arm around me and get comfortable.'

Steven seemed to relax, bare skin at my chest, firm bottom beneath my hand, knickers full of sex, a pouch of youthful tissue, growing, stiffening. My lips touched his cheek.

'You must not do that,' he said firmly.

I reached into the front of his knickers and gripped his lovely dick.

'I wish you wouldn't,' said the boy. 'Stop it, or I'll leave you and get in my own bunk.'

I let him go, put an arm round his neck, kissed his shiny hair.

'Please stay,' I said. 'I'm sorry. I don't really want to sleep alone tonight.'

'It's alright,' he replied. 'I understand perfectly. I'm lonely too, and I'll stay if you act sensibly.'

He unhooked the sarong from his waist, put it beneath the pillow. 'That's a bit cooler,' he said with a friendly smile. 'Will you settle down now?'

'Yes,' I said. 'I'll try my best.'

There was a fragrance in the cabin, the scent of pine and sandalwood, the perfume of the desert winds, the sweet smell of youth. Steven moved his body, brought his brown skin closer, touched me with his belly, made me glow. I looked at the sleeping boy's face, cool and quiet, even teeth and pink tongue, a very gentle young creature. His nearness comforted me. I took off my knickers and lay quite still. A slow Mediterranean roll sent us sideways and the boy's cool hand landed on my bottom.

'Mmmm!' The sigh of pleasure escaped from my lips. Steven began to feel me, a soft movement of the fingers that made my legs part.

'I shouldn't do this,' he murmured. 'It's not right.'

'You're not doing anything!'

He pulled the front of his knickers down and put his long dick on my skin. 'Would you like it up your bottom?' he asked, moving beneath me.

'Mmmm! Mmmm!'

'We shouldn't! he gasped. 'We really shouldn't be doing this.'

'Steven . . . Ooooh . . . Ooooh . . . Steven . . .'

'We shouldn't! We should not be doing this!' he panted. 'It's not right.'

'Mmmm! Mmmm!' I sighed. 'I know we shouldn't . . .'

9. Napoli, Napoli!

There she was! Dirty old Liverpool, dead ahead, seagulls on the wing, rusty old tramps in the stream, the Sally Army at the Pier Head — lousy music, old-fashioned bonnets, big brass instruments, scarlet-faced players, tinking tambourines, shit everywhere. Welcome home! Buy the *War Cry*! One penny!

Steven was taken by the immigration people. I didn't want to hang around and attend the *Tyndareus* enquiry; I wanted to ship out right away.

The food situation had improved — sausage and chips at Woolworth's cafeteria, spam and chips, spam and mash, spam fritters, spam and beans and onion gravy. Perhaps I'd find a berth on the spam boats.

Three old dolls named the Andrews Sisters had just hit the charts with a number called 'You Get No Bread With One Meat Ball'. The Yanks loved it and the English didn't know what a meat ball was. The average Joe knew spaghetti came in tins and the upper crust thought it grew in Italy — a Dago dish, what!

Italy, Mussolini and spaghetti, that's all they spoke about. It was in the papers, on the newsreels and blasting from the wireless sets. I guess it was more interesting than the cricket scores.

A clerk in the Shipping Federation leaned over the counter, pushed a slip of paper under my nose. 'I got a special one for you,' he said, 'a hospital ship, one of Elder Dempster's, a real beauty called the *Aba*. Get over to Birkenhead, She's signing on today.'

They were all still out there, everyone I knew: Jamie, Jackie Clithero, big Duffy, fighting on the beaches. I just hoped the hospital ship didn't bring them back in pieces.

The *Aba* was a real floating hospital, a sparkling white vessel with brilliant lights, bright red crosses, surgical wards, medical wards and lovely nurses of both sexes. I found a guy named Charlie Elliot in the pig and whistle, the ship's bar. He'd been at school with me, a ragged-arsed pupil at St Jude's.

'Hi Charlie!' I said. 'Where's she bound?'

'Italy,' said Charlie. 'We're taking a load of sick Italian prisoners.

It's a Red Cross deal, an exchange. We're bringing English and Yanks back.'

Charlie was the ship's butcher, so I guess he knew as much as the Shipping Federation and the War Office. It seemed the high rollers wanted a few reconditioned pawns in the game. Maybe the cannon fodder was running low.

Apart from a few wooden legs, a sprinkling of glass eyes and some artificial arms, the prisoners seemed a reasonably healthy bunch. I wondered what condition the exchange patients would be in. Perhaps they'd cop a £2 a week pension like Jacky Nolan.

Being among the patients made me cynical and unhappy, so I spent my time on deck. I suppose it was lonely, but I could handle loneliness. If I couldn't find the special companions I needed, then I didn't want anybody. Ordinary Joes meant nothing to me. I could be happy just staring at the ocean. It was very beautiful at night.

A ship's log hung from the after rail and spun in the depths of the sea. The casual observer would think it was a simple rope because they couldn't see the fin and wheel beneath the waves. The fin turned a wheel and the wheel turned a clock and the mechanism logged the knots and miles.

This simple apparatus created a phosphorescence and a myriad dancing lights that fascinated me. I was admiring its beautiful wash when Bobby Metcalfe came to my side and leaned over the rail. It was one of those nights, stars twinkling, ship ablaze with light, wonderful reflections in the water, salty spray in the wind.

Bobby didn't need colourful clothes. He was a natural — fresh pink cheeks, rich red lips, bright blue eyes and curly black hair. A real seafaring boy, a sixteen-year-old with nice clear skin and a fine athletic body.

'You're up here every evening,' he said.

'I like it,' I replied. 'It feels safe. I'm not used to sailing with the lights on. Feels kinda strange.'

'It scares me,' Bobby said. 'We can be seen for miles, Red Cross or no Red Cross. I don't think we're going to make it. Some bastard is going to blow us out of the water.'

I put my arm around his shoulder. He felt good, cuddly and receptive, a friendly young companion.

His mother had a small family hotel in Blackpool so we talked about her. He was very close to his mother but not a mummy's darling, just a concerned lad who had no father. I kissed him on the cheek. Bobby didn't object, so we moved into the shadows. Bobby leaned back against the bulkhead and I kissed him again.

'What was that for?' he said.

'I dunno. Just one of those things. I couldn't help it.'

'Do you like kissing boys?' asked Bobby.

'Yes,' I said. 'Do you mind?'

'It's alright,' Bobby said. 'I like being with you.'

We came close, lips touched gently, his hand went up my shirt and stroked my bare skin. My knees trembled. 'Bobby, I could kiss you all over,' I gasped, 'every inch of you.'

'Well, you'll have to wait until we get into one of my mum's double beds,' he said softly.

'Do you mean it?'

'Do you?' asked the boy in his lilting Lancashire voice.

I'd never experienced such absolute pleasure. He sent my heart leaping, dancing with joy.

'I've been searching for a boy like you all my life.'

'Well, now you've found me,' Bobby said.

We became very close as the days passed, and the evening kisses filled our lonely souls. Nothing else happened. It wasn't necessary. We lived in different cabins and could not have found the required privacy.

'Will you come ashore with me when we hit Naples?' I asked.

'I'd go anywhere with you,' replied Bobby.

'The same goes for me,' I said, nibbling at his ear.

He knew it was my birthday in a couple of days time. I'd mentioned it as a kind of joke, saying that I hadn't spent a Christmas or birthday at home since I was thirteen years old.

'We'll have a birthday party in Naples, ' said Bobby.

The *Aba* was a famous vessel, a well-known sight in every war zone with a record unequalled by any hospital ship. She had been machine-gunned, dive-bombed, holed in more than fifty places, had flying shrapnel in the wards, lifeboats shattered by enemy fire, been deliberately attacked by twelve Junker 85s and rescued by seven destroyers and two cruisers. Every ship in Naples harbour saluted her with screaming whistles and ear-piercing sounds. Crews lined their ship rails and waved dirty vests and shirts. She gave aid to the sick and wounded of any nationality, and everybody knew it.

Bobby was waiting for me on deck, looking very smart and handsome. He wore a beautifully tailored jacket and a silver merchant navy badge gleamed in his lapel. He looked so sweet and innocent that I felt a pang of guilt, but I had no intention of leading him astray.

'You look terrific!' I said admiring his gorgeous hair and smart outfit. 'I think I'll go back to my cabin and pick up a jacket.'

'Don't waste your time,' replied my handsome young friend. 'The skipper won't allow any of the crew ashore and the bloody purser won't dish out any money.'

The crew members had completed their job. The ship had arrived safe and sound and the exchange of prisoners would take place at some later date, so there seemed no sensible reason to withhold our shore leave. The unhappy crew members returned to their quarters and complained bitterly.

Young Bobby was itching to get ashore. 'What are we going to do?' he asked. 'Fuckin' daft bastards! Fancy tying a hospital ship, full of blazing lights and wounded men, alongside two friggin' great warships! They're gonna get blown outa the fuckin' water!'

A couple of short boarding gangways linked the *Aba* to the naval vessels. Some of our ship's officers and nursing staff were invited to join the Royal Navy officers in a little get-together. They put their smartest uniforms on and went aboard for the shindig in the gleaming saloons and glittering naval mess.

'I think we can scrounge a lift from one of the liberty ships,' I said to Bobby. 'Look! They're taking a few matelots ashore and the guys on the tiller are only naval ratings. Should we give it a try?'

'Suits me,' said my curly-headed friend, 'but I'm skint! I haven't got a fuckin' penny!'

'Nor me,' I replied, 'but I can get a pillow-case full of coffee. We can flog it! The people here in Naples must be desperate! The bleeding Germans are still moving out and I bet they've grabbed everything they could lay their friggin' hands on!'

A few minutes later we were up on deck again and ready to go. Speedy little liberty boats came and went. 'This kid looks alright,' I said to my mate. 'Are you ready?'

'Let's go!' said bonny Bobby and we stepped aboard a motor launch. The young sailor in charge looked at me kinda old-fashioned and I smiled at him and said, 'Taxi!'

'Cheeky bastard!' he countered. 'Scouse, ain't yer?'

'Fucken' right!' I replied. 'Everton.'

'Scotland Road,' answered the matelot. 'What's in the pillow case?'

'My laundry,' I replied. 'What do you think it is? Opium?'

'You'd better sit on it,' remarked the kid. 'Here comes one of our petty officers . . . Any more for shoreside!'

We stepped ashore with the naval ratings and headed for the Via Roma. 'Holy Christ!' said my astonished sidekick. 'Look at the bastards! Poor miserable buggers . . . just look at them.'

'Hey Joe,' shouted a ragged street-urchin. 'Wanna fuck my sister? Fifty lire!'

'You got chew gum, Americano?' asked another little boy.

'Sorry kid! What a fucken' war, Bobby.'

He was too busy chasing off the starving children to reply.

'Hey mister! Wanna jigi-jig? Fucki-fuck? Wanna sell food?'

'Mangiare! Mangiare! Food! Food!'

'Two cigarettes . . . fuck my sister!'

'Hey Americano!'

'We ain't Americans, kid!'

'Wanna small boy?'

'Piss off!'

'Wanna big boy? Mangiare! Food! Wanna screw?'

We were swamped by starving children and women in rags. It was getting out of hand and beginning to look dangerous when a young boy about thirteen years old came to our rescue.

'Andare! Andare!' he shouted angrily and shooed them all away.

'Largo! Largo!' he screamed at the persistent ones. They cleared off and went in search of richer pickings.

'What's in da bag?' enquired our ragged young rescuer. 'I buy anything. You want booze? Dames? Small boys? You name it, I gottit! What's in da bag?'

'Coffee,' said Bobby.

'Andiamos!' said our new friend. 'Let's go! Follow me!' He took us down a rubble-strewn street and into a nearby bar. We quite expected it to be a dump and were very much surprised by the smart and super-modern interior. It was just like a first-rate nightclub or modern American restaurant that you see on the movies.

'Some joint!' I whispered to Bobby. 'We should be safe in here.'

'Naturally,' replied my friend. 'This is the centre of town.'

It was hard to think of this pile of rubbish and Yankee equipment as a thriving city centre. Bobby's presence of mind and cool acceptance of the situation surprised me. I was on the look-out for danger all around.

'Mario,' shouted our ragged companion at the waiter. 'Due Americani per Mario!'

'Si, capisco,' replied the smart-looking waiter. He sat us at an empty table, placed an ashtray and a couple of empty glasses in front of us and went in search of Mario.

A handsome guy about thirty-five years old came in from the back room. He gave a friendly salute to the lad. 'Ciao, Pepino,' he said. 'Scram outa here and make some business!'

Pepino lifted his skinny frame from the comfort of Mario's restaurant. 'So long, Johnny!' he shouted to Bobby and pushed through the door, pockets crammed with dirty lire notes and a cheeky smile on his sun-tanned young face.

'How ya doin?' asked the well-dressed man. 'You guys offa ship? I'm Mario.'

'Yes,' I said. 'We only tied up today. We aren't supposed to be ashore really.'

'No foolin',' he said with a smile on his face. 'What's in da bag?'

'Coffee,' I explained. 'We couldn't draw any wages so we drew some coffee from the stores.'

Bobby laughed. 'Good job we ain't onna fuckin' banana boat,' he said, 'or we'd have been torn limb from limb by the kids.'

Mario joined us at the little table. 'Wanna beer?' he asked. 'Glassa vino? Piece-a ass?'

Bobby asked for vino, and I nodded my head in agreement.

Mario snapped his fingers. 'Comin' right up, fellers! You know somepin? I'm an American. Been in da States all my goddam life . . . den dey trew me out! Canya beetdat? Dey trew me outa da goddam States! Goddamit! How much for da coffee?'

The waiter put a carafe of wine on the table and Mario gave him the pillow-case. Bobby tasted the wine.

'Hey! It's good stuff, Rob,' he said. 'Knock it back! It's your birthday, remember!'

'Cheers, Bobby! All the best!'

Mario filled a glass for himself. 'Cin, cin' he said and took a tiny sip.

'We don't care about the coffee,' I said to Mario. 'We just need enough cash for a night out and the price of a hotel room for the two of us. We sneaked ashore on a navy boat and won't be able to get aboard our own ship until she ties up at the quayside some time tomorrow. If the coffee isn't enough to cover it, we can bring some food tomorrow. Will you trust us?'

'Da goddam coffee is like gold dust,' replied Mario. 'Hell! If it's a night out you want, go to da PX. I'll give you some dough. Go to da PX an' have a ball! Dey got all kindsa dames! Real cansa Schlitz! Pabst! Hooch! You name it, dey gottit! I wish to hell I could get inda goddam joint! Goddam cocksuckers!'

Bobby emptied his glass. 'That's not for us,' he said quietly. 'We can have a piss-up any time of the day or night. We've got our own bar on the ship and booze costs practically nothing. We really want to have a look around Naples and spend the night in a safe place until tomorrow when we can walk aboard the ship.'

'Cute kid!' said Mario. He snapped his fingers and the waiter brought another carafe of wine. Mario turned his attention to me. 'If you wanna see the sights,' he said, 'don't stay out very late. Finish your evening in my joint. It livens up later on. Guys drop rocks on your goddam head offa de buildings . . . so like I said, don't stay out late an' keep outa da shadows.'

He seemed too friendly to be true. Bobby offered the smokes around and Mario's lips drooled. 'You gotta lotta dem Camels an' Luckies onna ship?' he enquired.

'Fuckin' ship full!' replied my mate. 'Take the pack. Rob's got enough for us two for the night.'

The place began to liven up and Mario went about his business. A guy played the piano and, as the night moved on, we settled down and enjoyed ourselves. 'You happy here?' asked Bobby.

'Great!' I answered. 'Look at the kid who brought us here in the first place. He's wearing a friggin' evening dress!'

It was the boy Pepino. He sat at our table. 'Hi Johnny!' he said cheekily. 'You gonna get drunk! Drink aqua minerale. Vino kicks ya head in!'

'No chance, Pepino. We won't get dunk. You drink the fuckin' mineral water.'

Mario came over, threw a bundle of scruffy notes on the table and sat down. 'Money ain't worth shit!' he said disgustedly. 'I coulda bought a hotel for that much! Now goddam it . . .'

Pepino cleared up the glasses, brought a fresh ashtray and went about his business among the tables and drinking guests.

'You kids enjoying yourselves?' asked Mario.

'Wonderful!' replied Bobby. 'We're not going out. We'll spend the evening here and then find a hotel.'

'Cute kid!' remarked our host again. It seemed to be his special way of describing my young friend and I couldn't argue with him on that score. He wouldn't let us pay for any drinks, and kept asking us searching little questions that seemed innocent enough on the surface.

'What's da gun for?' he enquired. 'You scareda bein' hijacked?'

'What the hell for?' I asked. 'A bag of fucken' coffee! That's a joke.'

'So maybe you ain't what you seem,' replied the shrewd character. 'Maybe you got more dan a bag a fuckin' coffee! Da kid here works wid you, don' he? An' you got access to da goddam stores! You wid me?'

'Uh uh!'

'So maybe we can talka deal! Like legsa beef . . . canned goods . . . any goddam thing like food an' medicine. People are hungry here! You wit me so far?'

I took a sip of wine. 'I've been hungry myself,' I admitted.

'I ain't exactly laying it on da line,' replied Mario, 'but ya have ta admit dat I treated ya square so far!'

'Agreed,' muttered Bobby, by now increasingly stoned. 'If I

had my way I'd raid the friggin' butcher shop an' feed all the bloody kids in Naples.' Mario rumpled my young friend's hair with a hefty paw and said, 'Goddam lovely kid!'

I didn't mind. It was quite obvious to me that the guy was only interested in surviving and getting hold of some food, like everyone else in the stricken city. 'If you guys are interested,' said Mario, 'I'll tell you how to get da stuff off your ship. You won't have to carry anything outa da goddam docks. Leave all dat to me and I'll take care of da money. I'll pay you well.'

'How about the money?' I asked. 'You said it ain't worth shit!'

'Can you use invasion money?' he asked. 'I gotta fuckin' cellar full.'

'It's as good as dollars to us,' I replied. 'We can spend it anywhere in the world!'

'Betcha ass!' agreed Mario. He went over to the crowded bar and told a couple of British soldiers to take it easy.

'What the hell's invasion money?' whispered Bobby.

'Money that's printed by the British and American armed forces,' I replied. We can use it anywhere! It comes in five shilling notes, ten bob notes and Yankee dollar bills.'

Bobby seemed to be straightening up again. 'Are you alright?' I asked.

'Sure I am,' said my happy friend. 'I'm used to drinking wine. It hit me at first but I feel nice and mellow now. My mother serves wine at every meal. Wait till you meet her, Rob. You'll fall in love with her!' He swigged another glass of wine and smiled at me. 'Drink up,' he urged. 'It's your birthday.'

'Cin, cin, Bobby!'

'And you, Rob. What do you think of this guy Mario?'

'I'm not sure,' I answered. 'He's a clever bastard. I know that much. Did you know I was carrying a gun?'

'No,' said my friend. 'Do you think we can trust him?'

'What have we got to lose?' I asked. 'I'm enjoying myself.'

'So am I,' replied Bobby. 'I like this joint and I enjoy the Italian guy's company. He makes me feel like some movie gangster! But we might find ourselves in trouble if we pinch the fuckin' ship's stores.'

Mario came over with a bottle of spumanti. 'A birthday present for you,' he said with a wicked grin on his face. 'Play ball wid me, and I'll pay you fifty/fifty invasion money and lire. Waddya say?'

'I'm interested,' said my mate.

'Me too,' I echoed. 'Definitely!'

'See ya later,' said our host and walked through the swing doors leading to the kitchens.

'I'm hungry,' said Bobby. 'Are you?'

'Yeah! I'm hungry for my birthday cake.'

Bobby spluttered and the spumanti almost choked him.

Young Pepino came over to our table with a couple of plates of spaghetti and meat balls. 'Signorini,' he said in his lovely soft Neapolitan voice. 'I call you the very young gentlemen. I do not like the word signor. Buon appetito! Lei capisce?'

'Capisco,' I replied.

'Grazie,' said young Bobby. 'Molto grazie, Pepino.'

'Prego,' replied the friendly kid. 'Tink nottin' of it, you guys!'

'We must be eating his bloody dinner,' said Bobby. I feel quite guilty.' He got stuck into the spaghetti nevertheless.

'I bet they speak German as well as American,' Bobby offered after a minute or so, his mouth still full of spaghetti.

'They'll be speaking every friggin' language in Europe soon,' I replied. 'All the fuckin' armies of the world will pass through here before the end of the year. Turks, Greeks, Indians, Poles. Jesus! This place will be the poxhole of the world!'

The music flattened our conversation. Soldiers came and went, and a few shady deals took place in the back room. We didn't see anything special but we certainly knew there was something going on.

'When you want to hit da sack,' said Mario. 'just let me know. You can't go out dis time of night. You'll be rolled and robbed of your papers. I'm sending you to a little albergo across the street.' He called Pepino over. 'Ask da old bitch for a nice room and a letto grosso for my English friends. Capisce?'

We had a few more laughs with some Highland soldiers and smoked a couple of fat cigars from an American sergeant. Mine had 'Five Cents' stamped on it. 'How much is five cents?' I asked Bobby. 'What does it say on yours?' He rolled the fragrant weed in his fingers. 'It says "Compliments of the Havana Cigar Company. Not to be sold to any member of the public".' My cigar smelt lovely and made me feel quite dizzy.

A few German soldiers came into the bar. They had 'British Free Corps' printed on their shoulders. It felt like it was time to go, so we signalled to Pepino.

'Andiamos!' he shouted above the din. 'Follow me!'

'Keep your wits about you, Bobby,' I suggested. 'The key word is pericolo.'

'What the hell is that?' asked the innocent lad.

'Danger! Keep your wits about you. This kid could be leading us to a fuckin' meat ball machine. Pericolo!'

Bobby didn't seem to care. He was enjoying himself and laughed out loud. 'It's like Sweeny Todd the barber,' he said, 'only we finish in the spaghetti instead of the meat pies. Holy Christ! I'm as drunk as a monkey.'

Busy little jeeps flashed by in the darkness of the night, packed with drunken GI Joes and whores, no lights other than the glowing cigar butts. They were laughing Americans on their way to a good night out, a song on their lips and the memory of the bitter fighting forgotten for the moment. 'I love it!,' shouted Bobby. 'Goddamn it! I love it! It's like being in a John Wayne movie!'

Pepino led us into a medium-sized albergo — an inn or family hotel — with a well-carpeted lounge, solid-looking highly polished furniture and a sparkling, modern-type American bar with a most mouth-watering display of wines and liqueurs on the colourful glass shelves.

'Nice place,' remarked Bobby. 'Does it belong to Mario?'

'Si,' answered our young guide. 'Mario, da big boss, il capo. Capisce?'

'I understand,' replied my mate. 'Mario must be loaded!'

'Loaded?' enquired the youngster, puzzled look on his face.

'Plenty of lire!' explained Bobby.

'Plenny a dough! Ya goddam right. Plenny a dough an no spaghetti! Mario is better dan de pope a fuckin' Roma. Feeds all da goddam kids in Napoli! I show you da big boss, domani ... tomorrow, you see!'

An elderly lady, dressed head to foot in black, smiled on us and stroked Pepino's well-groomed hair. 'Ciao, bambino,' she greeted him.

'Nonna!' answered the lad. 'Come sta?'

His grandmother spread her neat little hands palms upward, looked into the ancient timbered ceiling, opened her mouth in despair and said, 'Dio mio! Per l'amor di Dio!'

She didn't speak any English, and our Italian was slightly limited to say the least.

'Avete stanze da affittare?' asked Pepino.

'Si. Per la notte?' asked the old lady.

Pepino shrugged his shoulders. 'Una, due, tre. Chissa? Una camera con un letto grosso per favore. Amici di Mario. Capisce, Nonna?'

She understood alright. While we were trying to work it all out, she picked up a bunch of keys from the bar, smiled at her grandson and said, 'Andiamos.' We were learning fast, and followed her up the richly carpeted stairs.

'Buona notte!' shouted Pepino. 'Buona notte, amici!'

The room was excellent: spotlessly clean, high-ceilinged with velvet-covered chairs on the beautiful Persian carpet and heavy, hand-embroidered drapes at the windows, an oaken sideboard decorated with Venetian glassware and an inlaid coffee table with a cut-glass ashtray in the centre. She led us through a partly opened door and into a bedroom fit for a king.

'Un letto grosso,' she said proudly, pointing to an enormous four-poster bed that dominated the room. It must have been hundreds of years old. The great posts gleamed with years of polished pride and joy; a huge canopy of light purple material stretched across the frame like some ancient Arabian tent from my fairy-tale books and thick embroidered drapes matching those at the windows reached right down to the luxurious carpet beneath our feet.

The old lady put the keys down on a little side-table, said 'Buona notte, signori,' and slipped away quietly on her black and silent slippered feet.

'What a room!' said Bobby. 'Christ! If my old lady had a bed like that, she'd have a sign on the promenade at Blackpool: "Queen Anne slept here!" It's like going back in time. I can picture the three musketeers or the man in the iron mask . . .' He kicked off his shoes and dived onto the enormous bed. 'Fuckin' hell!' he shouted. 'I'll go to sleep and never wake up.'

I pulled the drapes and sat on the other side of the bed to undress.

'This is a bit different from kissing on the deck of the ship,' said Bobby. 'I've not slept with a guy before.'

'Don't worry about it,' I said over my shoulder.

Bobby removed his shirt, walked over to the window in his trousers and opened the curtains. 'Did you see where the bathroom is?' he asked.

'I never noticed,' I replied. 'Piss out the window.'

We sank into the gorgeous bed. Bobby gripped my fingers. We just had to kiss; there was nothing we could do about it. We loved kissing one another, and knew perfectly well it would lead to something far more exciting.

Bobby stroked my cheek with the back of his fingers. 'Did you get that conversation between Pepino and his nonna?' he asked, nibbling at my ear. 'I think he told her we were taking the room for two or three nights.'

I kissed his soft cheek and held him close. 'I hope you're right,' I answered.

He nuzzled into me like a warm little puppy and kissed my eyelids, my throat and my chest. 'I like kissing you,' said sweet Bobby. Our lips touched very light and gentle. dry and sweet, real boys' kisses that I loved so very much.

'I've kissed boys before,' I said in turn.

'You don't see anything wrong with it then?'

'Not with you, Bob. You're sweeter than any girl.'

'I don't go with girls,' admitted Bobby. 'Do you?'

'No,' I said quietly. 'I don't like girls. I couldn't love a girl.'

We held each other very close, kissed and stroked gently at cheeks and hair. 'Could you love a boy?' whispered the lad.

'I do,' said I. 'I love a boy.'

Bobby pulled me close against him. 'I'm hard as a rock,' he whispered.

'You're too young and innocent,' I replied. 'Keep your shorts on, Bobby. I don't want to spoil things.'

'You said you wouldn't.'

'I will if your shorts come off. You're a beautiful boy. I'm surprised no one has had you before now.'

'I'm not so innocent!' said lovely Bobby. 'I've fooled around with my cousin back home. Momma put us in the same bed every weekend. We didn't do anything serious.'

I hugged him close and kissed his nose. Nobody got seduced that first night in the four-poster. Nature just stepped in and took a hand in the game. Bronzed young bodies, pressed naked against each other; toes, knees, warm bare chests and muscular bellies. We looked into each other's eyes, noses touching, and hot fluid splashed onto our skin sticking us together like glue.

'Rob?'

'Shh, Bobby. Go to sleep.'

'Don't let go of me!'

'I'll never let you go,' I whispered softly.

The beautiful song 'Santa Lucia' is a barcarolle, a boat song of the Neapolitan gondoliers which describes the gentle blue waves of the bay of Naples. It came soft and melodious through the open window and awakened us. Bobby looked into my eyes and I kissed the blushing boy on his forehead. 'I love you,' I said sincerely.

'I know you do,' replied my friend. 'I love you too, Rob. Will you always be my shipmate?'

'Always, Bobby. Always. I'll never leave you.'

'He kissed my lips, peeled our bodies carefully apart and got out of bed. 'I guess we know now,' Bobby said as he made use of the primitive sanitary arrangements and cleaned himself up.

We hit the Via Roma and made our way to Mario's restaurant. Pepino met us on the strada. He was dressed in his workaday rags, and touting for the boss he so obviously adored.

'Buon giorno!' he greeted us with a smile. 'Come! I take you to see Mario.'

The retreating armies had left a hell of a mess. Bridges were down; gas mains, water mains and electricity supplies were damaged and unsafe. Air raids were not uncommon, and the city was in a state of emergency.

The able-bodied men had fled, leaving only the old, the children and the frightened women. A loaf of bread that cost ten lire on Monday cost a thousand on Tuesday. There was no common language. Conversation took place in a mixture of foreign tongues; long-forgotten schoolboy French, snatches of any Latin tongue that remained in your head from a pre-war holiday on the Continent, bits of Arabic picked up from the Middle East, sign language and a lot of American slang from the proud Yankee schoolchildren: six feet tall, chewing gum, toting firearms and dressed like soldiers.

No one could count so everything was done in round figures. It was much easier to say twenty, fifty or a hundred — venti, cinquanta, cento — but when it came to odd numbers like seventeen or forty-three, people just made a joke of it, settling for the nearest round figure they could understand. This didn't help with the inflation problem.

Money would remain worthless until the conquering heroes reached an agreement with what was left of the local government. These people argued among themselves, split up into splinter groups and added to the total confusion by fighting, back-biting and seeking control.

We were quite amazed to see Mario in action. He was a villain, without a doubt; the USA does not throw law-abiding citizens out of the land of liberty without some good reason. However, Mario seemed to be the only person in Naples who knew what he was doing. Hundreds of worn-out housewives and poor children formed a queue, half in and half out of a ruined church. Mario was feeding them with the help of a few American GI Joes. He wore an ankle-length white apron and was dishing out plates of spaghetti and meat sauce.

Two hard-eyed, villainous-looking mountain men or deserters sat watching. They seemed to be his personal bodyguard. The American Joes were dishing out all kinds of goods that belonged to the US forces and had been hijacked. Americans are a kind and caring people. They want to be loved and they gave their own candy bars and K rations to the poor kids too. No doubt there were many British soldiers in Naples, but Bobby and I hardly saw them. It was an American city as far as we were concerned. Perhaps the British occupied other cities. Anyway, the British troops had no candy bars, chewing gum, fat cigars or bottles of whisky on the hip. Nor did they possess such things as K rations and ice-cream fridges. They were lucky if they had a packet of Woodbines or a pair of dry socks.

Mario passed his ladle to one of the GIs, wiped his hands on his apron and came across to Pepino. He stroked the lad's head in a fatherly manner and said, 'Ciao Pepino, go do some hustling!'

'You get da message?' he asked. 'I'm a goddam saint! Saint Mario da foist! Waddya know about dat?'

'We'll go along with you,' said Bobby. 'Tell us what to do.'

'Dump a coupla legsa beef, pork chops, sidesa bacon, stuff like dat. Gottit? Cut dem up an' trow dem in da trash cans. Take da goddam trash cans an line dem up with all da udda shit on the quay-side. Open a coupla cansa raspberry jam and trow da goddam stuff on top; make it messy; jagged can lids an all kindsa flies buzzin' around . . . big heapa shit! You wit me?'

'What happens if someone gets nosey?' we asked.

'Dey won't,' said Mario. 'Dat's da harbour-master's orders; all trash on da dockside; no rubbish in da goddam water. If you can, trow a few empty cartons of canned goods among the crap — mix 'em wid torn empty cartons an' old newspapers. My boys will do da rest and you won't get into any trouble. I don' haveta spell it out, do I? I mean, you ain't stoopid!'

'We'd like to leave our coats with you,' I said. 'We'll need to walk into the docks in our shirt-sleeves. That way they'll think we just slipped ashore for a few minutes. We're supposed to be working today.'

Bobby slipped out of his expensive jacket and removed his tie.

'Put your tings in da hotel room,' said Mario, returning to his feeding operations. 'You have da suita rooms poimanent! Okay?'

We thanked him and made our way back to the hotel.

On the way to the docks we were stopped by a gleaming American military cop, snow-white helmet on his head and automatic weapon at the ready. 'Where you guys headed?' asked the 'snowdrop', all fierce and business-like. 'Lemme see your papers!'

Bobby produced his seaman's ID card.

What ship?' asked the snowdrop.

'Hospital ship *Aba*,' I replied, fumbling in my back pocket for my ID.

You got any funny papers aboard?' asked the military man. 'Any comic books or magazines?'

The quayside was a hive of activity — stores and busy chain-gangs of men working them aboard by hand — and the ridiculousness of the situation took me by surprise.

'We've got a fuckin' ship full of comics and magazines,' answered Bobby quick as a flash. 'Where can we find you?'

'In the MPs' hut,' replied the soldier. 'Just walk in and ask for Kookie. That's me,' he added proudly.

'Okay, Kookie, See ya later!'

'Gee! Thanks guys!'

'Prego,' remarked Bobby. 'Think nothing of it, pal!'

We walked up the gangway, almost wetting our trousers with laughter.

'Where you two pricks been?' asked Charlie the butcher. He was much senior to us; a ship's officer if he wished to assert his authority. The merchant navy is a crazy little world of its own. Chief stewards, chefs, and other important departmental chiefs seldom wear a uniform. They all have rank but very seldom use it except to keep their own department running smoothly at sea.,

Bobby started laughing. 'What's so funny?' asked the butcher. 'And where the hell you been?'

'We've been in the MPs' hut all morning,' said Bobby.

'Bollocks,' replied Charlie. 'You've been ashore. Anyway, it's no skin off my fuckin' nose. The purser is paying out in the main saloon. Get your morning's work done. Christ knows what's going to happen aboard this friggin' tub until we exchange the prisoners.'

'How about shore leave?' asked Bobby.

'Port and starboard watches,' replied the butcher. 'I'm pissing off for the day!'

Port and starboard watches meant that one half of the crew was free for shore leave and the other half would be free the next day, but everyone except the nursing orderlies could go ashore after duty. There was always an older guy who had seen everything in the universe and was willing to do a stand-in for any younger guy who wanted to go ashore, so it wasn't important. The purser paid us out in pound notes and advised us to be careful if we exchanged these anywhere except at those official banks that were open. I managed to throw a few things in the 'rosy' and pack a couple of cartons of goods from the stores just as Mario had advised. I was on duty anyway, dishing out goods to the different departments and cleaning out the stores.

Hundreds of troops still had to be fed; the butchers and bakers and candlestick makers of the world can't stop to visit Naples.

Bobby met me in the glory hole. 'I wrapped a few things in greaseproof paper,' he said when he got the chance. 'I hope we don't poison some poor bastard. I cut them up just like Mario said and bunged them in the swill bins with burlap and cardboard.'

163

We stepped on deck. The harbour was alive with shipping: cruisers, frigates, cargo boats and troop ships. Armour-plated guns bristled from every deck and thick rope scrambling nets hung from the battle-grey sides of ships as far as the eye could see.

'Holy Jesus!' I remarked. 'Looks like there's a friggin' war on! Give us a lift with a couple of dustbins, kid. I can't shift them by myself.'

Bobby helped me unload the loot. 'Do you think we'll be alright?' he asked.

'Look around you,' I replied.

The boy laughed. 'Look at the shit all over the friggin' place,' he said. 'Nobody would know what ship the stuff came from anyway.'

The Red Cross personnel aboard ship could supply us with all kinds of reading material, including whole libraries of modern paperbacks specially printed for US troops. There were no comic books, however, so we got changed into clean shirts and cotton slacks, and walked aboard a big liberty ship flying the stars and stripes.

There were lots of ships to choose from but this brand new super ship looked like it had just left the States for the first time. It was like a candy store. Gorgeous young American boys ran around in their underwear, smelling fragrant with deodorants and after-shave, body lotion and perfumes of all description. Young English lads hadn't reached this stage of civilised living as yet. The Americans treated us like long lost cousins and offered us anything we wanted. It's only fair to say that all seafarers treat guys from other ships in the same brotherly way. However, not many visitors ask for comics; it's usually a bottle of gin or an exchange of vodka for rum.

One dreamboat from west Texas caught us in the after well deck. 'I got something for you boys,' said the Texas rose. I just had to pinch his neat little bottom. There was something about the way young American seafarers wore their trousers that fascinated me.

The handsome youngster took us into his cabin and loaded us up with his treasure: a stack of Buck Rogers. He introduced us to a few more guys and we struck pay dirt: Flash Gordon, Little Orphan Annie, Dagwood Bumstead, Popeye and every Yankee comic you could possible think of.

We made some very pleasant friends among the American merchantmen and promised to join them for a party aboard ship some time before we sailed. The young Texan also gave us a couple of cans of shaving foam.

The stack of Buck Rogers was far too great a prize to part with right away, so we took the whole lot back to our ship, tucked the specials into a locker — in case we needed a special favour — and carried the remainder over to Kookie. He went potty when we tipped a kit bag full of comics at his feet and swore he'd be our friend for life. 'Wow! Flash Gordon! In colour! Gee whiz, fellers!!!!'

We moved off from the world of innocent young sailor boys, mom's apple pie and homemade cookies, and took a walk on the hot and dusty streets of Napoli. Tiny flies and buzzing mosquitos zinged in our ears, swarmed about our sweating faces and made us itch and slap. There was an epidemic of VD; bright red and white posters screamed out the message in huge capitals: 'DANGER! SYPHILIS!'

It was the first time in my life I had actually seen the written word. Of course, the common names of VD were used among servicemen, but to see such words in print was a new break through in the world as we knew it. If such a poster had been displayed in Great Britain, there would have been uproar and questions asked in Parliament. It could quite easily have interrupted the war news, if not the constant flow of cricket scores that came every hour of the day from the BBC. Even the Battle of Britain and the fall of Dunkirk had not been allowed to stop the cricket scores.

The dusty streets and smelly flies were getting the better of us when we came across a line of guys, perhaps two hundred strong. There were Poles, French legionnaires, US marines, Canadians, Indian sailors and British soldiers; guys from all the armies and navies of the world stood in line.

A bleary-eyed soldier stepped from the doorway of a paint-peeled house, buttonning his trousers.

'What goes on?' asked Bobby, all sweet and innocent. 'Hey soldier! What's going on?'

'Fuck all!' replied the soldier. 'It's a brothel! A short-time house. Fifty lire for a quick fuck. Don't slip on the French letters! There's a million in the fuckin' hallway.'

The line moved up and we walked around the corner, right into the arms of two American MPs. One of them must have been forty-five or fifty years old. 'Have you kids been in that whore-house?' asked the older one. 'It's against regulations but you can step inside and have some free shots.'

'Free shots?' we asked, open-mouthed and innocent.

He smiled and pointed with his club. 'Sure! In there! Free shots! They're for our own boys but they'll give you some. Merchant marine get treated along with our own.'

Bobby read the sign aloud: 'Syphilis injections! US forces only!'

'Thanks, pop!' we shouted, and walked off as fast as we could.

The snowdrop twirled his club. 'Kids!' he exclaimed. 'Goddam kids!'

Craters in the roads and pavements, archways dating back to ancient Rome, filthy old men and donkeys urinating in the two-thousand-year-old walled courtyards, superb buildings and breathtaking scenery, family washing strung across the broken roads . . . Wonderful fountains stood at the top of the long-stepped narrow streets where the Neapolitan city-dwellers lived. Filthy, paint-peeled shops displayed magnificent glassware and the ragged children sold their brothers and sisters on the streets for a cigarette . . .

'I'm glad I'm not one of them,' remarked my young friend.

'One of what?' I asked.

'Those guys! Those poor dumb bastards! Fancy queuing up for hours to fuck some dirty old bag and get a dose of the pox. They must be peculiar! There's something wrong with the silly buggers.'

'Not like you and me, eh Bobby?'

'Damn right! Jesus, I could use a shower!'

'We can rinse our faces in that fountain.'

'Piss off!' answered Bobby. 'We'd get fuckin' typhoid!'

'Let's try the American PX. They'll have showers.'

'Sounds good,' replied the lad.

The PX was located on the Via Roma. It was a magnificent building and looked like it had been a splendid hotel at one time. It was still intact, but now it was purely a place of refuge and entertainment. Rooms were available for American officers and important visitors from other Allied armies, but although the average GI Joe was welcome, British troops were barred.

This was quite a sensible arrangement, as the typical British soldier was jealous of his American cousin's high standard of pay and general way of life. Fighting often broke out when they got together.

Nor were black people allowed in the place. This was one of the more ridiculous things about the American way of life and caused dreadful scenes and battles among the troops. The land of liberty, equality and the rights of man was not quite as upright and decent as it appeared, but there was little to be done about it while the great nation held on tight to the madness of the colour bar.

Bobby and I were very lucky. The MPs who guarded the entrance to this imposing wonderland saluted and waved us in with a smile. The merchant navy carried American troops to every battle zone and were accepted all over the world. Strangely enough, a British sailor from the Royal Navy who risked his life at sea guarding the convoys of floating troops was banned, unless of course he was an officer with an armful of gold braid.

Less than thirty miles away vicious fighting was in progress, and men were bleeding to death on the beaches. Fortunately we didn't know about it. Bobby and I were far too happy beneath the hot showers, compliments of Uncle Sam. A friendly bathroom attendant offered us his services as a masseur, but he was more interested in masturbation. We declined his generous offer and accepted some perfumed body lotion instead.

Fresh and clean once again, we strolled the Via Roma and made our way to the albergo, planning our night of love as we walked. However, the ancient road overcame me with its magic.

'Every goddam army in the world has strolled this way,' I said to Bobby. 'The Roman legions walked this very pavement. Look at it! It's still as magnificent as ever, and I bet it hasn't changed in two thousand years.'

'Jackie Robbo, you are a fuckin' dreamer!' replied my companion. 'Forget about the ancient Romans. Who wants to look at a pile of fuckin' ruins? Let's hurry. I want to jump into bed with you.' We held hands in the shadows and trembled with love and tenderness.

Mario met us at the albergo and came upstairs to our room. 'Are you comfortable in here?' he asked, riffling Bobby's curls with his long brown fingers. Bobby looked across at me and I smiled reassuringly, knowing that he felt uncomfortable with the situation.

'We slept well last night,' I said. 'It's a beautiful suite of rooms.' Bobby kicked off his shoes and sat on a large chair by the window.

'We gotta drink coming up,' said Mario. 'You kids did goddam well today. I like da way you work an' da easy way you got round da dopey MP atta dockside.'

The old lady came into the room with two bottles of champagne. Mario opened one, filled three hollow-stemmed goblets and said, 'Here's to crime! Cin, cin!'

'Salute,' replied Bobby, draining his glass like it was his momma's orange squash.

'Cheers!' said I. 'You know, these are the most beautiful glasses I've seen in my life.'

'You can say dat again,' remarked Mario. 'All we got is wine, glasses an' goddam lemons! You ever try living on goddam lemons?'

I liked his crazy way with words and his terrific personality, but there was a hidden depth to him that I feared. I think it was because he knew too much and the fact that he'd obviously had us under surveillance. 'You've been spying on us,' said Bobby in his down-to-earth Lancashire way.

'For Christ's sake!' exclaimed Mario. 'It's my business to know what goes on. You wanna work wit some goddam meatball who dunno shit! Shee-it!' He filled the glasses up, and we thought things over.

'You wanna contact me any time?' Mario said, staring through the open window. 'You see dose tree guys playin' da barrel organ? Dey go all over town and dey hang around the harbour. Da old guy speaks English. Get me? You kids stick wid me an' you'll go home wid a lotta dough in your pants ... Holy Christ! Da fuckin' mountain is blowin' up! Let's get outa here!'

Vesuvius was indeed throwing flames into the sky and clouds of dust and sparks flew everywhere.

'Fuck this!' said Bobby. 'We better get back to the ship! The whole fuckin' city might be swallowed up. I think there's gonna be an earthquake! Let's go!'

Charlie met us on deck. 'She's gonna blow!' he shouted excitedly, pointing to the belching cone of Vesuvius. 'What's it like in the city?'

'Sparks!' replied Bobby. 'Fuckin' great red-hot sparks and smoke. You can't see your hand in front of your face. If the fuckin' wind changes we'll go up in flames! You'd think the fuckin' skipper would have the sense to pull outa here. Daft bastard!'

'For Christ's sake!' I said. 'I thought Vesuvius was extinct! The last time it went up was two thousand years ago!'

'Bollocks!' replied Bobby. 'You an' your fuckin' history! There she blows! Holy Jesus!'

'Don't forget Mary an' friggin' Joseph,' said Charlie. 'Let's get a couple of hoses on deck. Half the crew ain't aboard yet.'

It was like a scene from a Hollywood movie — a huge black mushroom, three separate streams of lava trying to form one gigantic river of fire as they rolled down the mountainside burning, destroying and obliterating everything in their path. Great red-hot lumps of rock flew through the air, burning bushes and great clumps of earth. It was frightening and grew worse with each passing moment.

Crew men from all over the world lined their ships' rails to witnesss the spectacle — bare-chested bronzed seafarers, greasers in filthy torn singlets and chefs in tall white hats.

Then the black cloud fell from the skies like fine graphite, choking the lungs, blinding and searing the eyes. We had to borrow military anti-gas goggles.

Ex-prisoners of war filled the hospital beds: naval guys, army men and troops who had been very near to death — so bad they were being exchanged so that they could die in their homeland. Some were on crutches and some were blind, thankful they were going home at last. It looked like we too would be saying, 'Arrividerci, Mario!', and it looked like farewell to the love nest and the sweet music beneath the window of the albergo.

'I told you something was gonna fuckin' happen!' said young Bobby. 'I knew it all along.'

The blazing volcano lit up the sky and things began to look pretty bad for old Napoli. The civilian population in certain quarters began to evacuate, packing up their goods and chattels. The air-raid sirens screamed out their terrifying wail and long brilliant searching fingers of light scoured the smoky skies in vain for enemy aircraft.

The *Aba* copped it at one-thirty in the morning. There was a terrrifying crash. 'Holy Christ!' shouted Bobby. 'I think we got a bomb right down the bleedin' funnel!' We rushed on deck. It looked as if Bobby was right, but there was so much to be done that we hardly knew what had happened.

Fire broke out. Shock! Burns! Broken bones! It was dreadful. Most of the patients had been in a bad enough way before it started. Now doctors with broken bones were trying to mend other poor guys with broken bones, and young ex-prisoners were crying for their mommas.

I can only see it now through a haze of little pictures stamped on my memory, and most members of the crew saw things from different angles and positions: broken crutches, frightened nurses and scared, wounded boys. But the nurses were indeed wonderful, male and female alike.

The crew came off best of all; only one member was killed outright, a quartermaster I had never set eyes on. One medical orderly was also killed in the D deck pantry on the port side, and one patient in the ward on D deck starboard. The bomb had passed through A deck and B deck, smashing all the superstructure as it went. It carried on through C deck and finally exploded on D deck. Eventually the fantastic medical staff, who had experienced similar mayhem on past voyages, settled the patients down. Some kind of order was restored, so Bobby and I went ashore to forget about it and get drunk. Naturally we dropped in on Mario.

Things went on very much the same; supplies went ashore and found their way into Mario's hands. Bobby and I moved back into the albergo and prepared for the wonderful night of love that had so far eluded us. However, Mario — who trusted us by this time — decided to put a new proposition to us. He wanted drugs and medicine. We objected and spoke about the wounded ex-prisoners aboard ship waiting to get home.

'Don' cry on my fuckin' shoulder,' Mario retorted. 'I seen a lot worse. At least dose poor bastards got medical care: doctors, nurses an' drugs. Dere's guys out dere inna mountains need stuff like dat. Italy is crawling with all kindsa patriotic groups, splinter groups an' guys who dunno which goddam side dey're fightin' on. Dey got nuttin'! Dey can't even report to a Red Cross station, so dey die out onna goddam mountain; bleed to death because dey ain't gotta goddam bandage and die of infected wounds.'

'So you want to supply them with black-market medicine and drugs?'

'Ain't talkin' about chopped liver!' replied the man. 'If you knew where da money came from you wouldn't care two goddam cents! An anudda ting! Scruples! You got scruples? You cain't eat goddam scruples! What would have happened if all da medicine had been destroyed in da bombin'?'

'I suppose we'd have got some more from the supply depot,' answered Bobby.

'Ya goddam right!' said Mario.

Mario left us, and when the door of our bedroom was finally closed, all the brash talk about how we were going to make love and the things we were going to do with each other seemed to fade into insignificance. We discussed the rights and wrongs of things and finally agreed to play ball, which meant simply smuggling two of his men aboard the ship the following night.

There is no justification for stealing medical supplies and there is no justification in denying medical supplies to people who need them, friend or foe. The dreadful thing is, I think we did it for the money.

'I think we should go to bed,' said Bobby. 'We'll be sitting here all night worrying about it.'

We undressed, and jumped into bed.

The streets of Naples were still thick with the falling lava dust when we awoke and kissed. We washed, dressed, kissed once more, then made our way to the rendezvous with Mario's thieves.

'I love all this!' Bobby said excitedly. 'I feel like a real baddy in a movie. Was it as exciting as this when you were in South Africa?'

'It was different,' I replied. 'There was no friggin' lava dust choking me to death.'

'Do you think Mario was a gangster when he was in the States?' asked Bobby.

'You can't believe anything, kid. Maybe he never was in the fuckin' States for all we know.'

'I feel like an adventurer,' he replied.

'Well, you ain't a mummy's darling!' I said sincerely. 'Just remember, we could still get into serious trouble and we still have time to back out. Fuck Mario.'

'I'm going through with it,' replied the kid.

Kookie was on duty when we approached the docks with two of Mario's men — four white-shirted stewards, arm in arm and slightly drunk. 'Hi Kookie,' shouted Bobby. I stopped and showed my ID card and the others simply walked on. 'We've got a stack of Buck Rogers for you,' I said. 'Come aboard with us and pick them up.'

'I can't leave my post,' replied the sentry.

'Never mind,' I said, lighting a cigarette. 'We'll bring them over in a few minutes.'

'The two men were safely stowed away in an empty cabin by the time I got aboard. Bobby was waiting for me in the glory hole.

'Let's go see Kookie,' I suggested. 'Bring the comics and don't act too drunk.'

He was sitting in the MPs' hut, cleaning an automatic weapon, when we walked in on him.

'You ever use that thing?' I asked jokingly. 'It looks fucken' deadly.'

Kookie picked up the submachinegun, pointed it to the ceiling and made a noise with his mouth like a kid playing soldiers: 'Bubba, bubba, bubba . . . I ain't bin in the shootin' war yet,' he said, 'but goddam it! When I get there . . .' He spun on his heels playing soldiers again. We gave him the comic books and Bobby put his hand on the deadly-looking weapon.

'Can I pick it up?' he asked.

Kookie looked questioningly at the sergeant in charge. 'Let the kid have it,' said the big guy with the stripes. 'Take the goddam magazine out first, you creep!'

The sergeant opened up a Buck Rogers comic and smiled as he thought of his good old days in Noo Joisey or wherever. Bobby played at shooting down imaginary aircraft for a few seconds and we returned to the ship delighted with ourselves. We were home and dry! Whatever took place in the night was none of our business.

The medical stores were duly ransacked and the stuff went over the side in sealed containers. Mario paid us off, saying we would do a lot more business deals together. I believed him, because he always knew exactly what he was talking about.

It was time to say, 'Arrivederci, Napoli!' Young Pepino embraced us openly on the strada. We would miss his cheeky smile and worldly ways. Mario produced three glasses of rich Marsala, and embraced us just as warmly. We said goodbye and set sail for England.

10. The Greatest Show on Earth

The shipping pool was packed with seamen. Pictures of General Eisenhower, Winston Churchill and Joe Stalin lined the dusty walls. A framed portrait of Our Sovereign Lord The King hung above the central desk. Georgie was the third monarch I'd known on the throne, a thin-faced man, rows of gleaming medals on his naval uniform, ridiculous shoulder epaulettes, Admiral of the Fleet, Ruler of Great Britain and Ireland, Defender of the Faith, Emperor of India, born to rule the mighty British Empire.

Hand-drawn signs hung from the ceiling: Special Operations This Way!

'What's it all about?' we asked the clerk.

'Combined Operations,' he replied. 'Sign the Official Secrets Act. There's extra pay involved.'

'What's the extra pay for?'

'How the hell do I know?' asked the guy. 'Sign the act and piss off! There's a big queue behind you.'

Everyone knew it was the big show, the second front, the invasion of Europe, but no one could really believe it.

Special operations didn't bind us to a single ship; we came under the direct control of a particular harbour master, and he could place us where he wished. Bobby and I were allotted the *El Nil*, an Egyptian vessel tied up in Middlesborough. There was no special rush; she wasn't going anywhere for a while, and we had seven days in which to join her.

There was a phone box outside the Shipping Federation. I picked up the receiver, put two pennies in the slot and dialled a number in east Lancashire.

Jamie answered my telephone call. 'I've been expecting you,' he said. 'Mom says you've been ringing every day. Are you in Blackpool at the moment?'

'No,' I said. 'I'm in Liverpool with my shipmate. Should I call and visit you?'

'Stay where you are,' he replied. 'I'll catch the train and get to Central station in less than an hour.'

'How about Bobby?'

'I'm dying to meet him,' said Jamie. 'What's he like?'

'Gorgeous,' I said. 'Just like you. See you in an hour, kid.'

There was something strange about Central station. I always felt uncomfortable in the steamy confines, with the clang of steel and rusty iron, rattling wheels and thumping metal chains. No other railway station affected me but this one did. Perhaps the sounds were amplified, increased by the long dark tunnels that led to the Mersey railway and the frightening journey beneath the salty river.

A red and black engine came thundering down the track, steam clouds shooting from the stumpy stack, a dirty face at the cab opening, dozens of carriages rattling behind. The whistle screamed and the throng of people on the platform moved expectantly. The train came to a halt. Scores of carriage doors opened and hundreds of soldiers and sailors leapt out. Their loved ones met them with open arms, a familiar scene at every railway station in the war-torn world.

Bobby nudged me in the ribs. 'There's your mate,' he said, 'the guy with the blue wings on his shoulder. Jesus! No wonder you fell for him.'

Jamie spotted us. I moved towards him hands apart. He put his gas mask and a small pack on the deck, straightened up and smiled his lovely smile. We hugged, and my lips touched his smooth cheek. He rocked back on his heels, held me close and kissed the side of my face.

'Where the hell you bin?' I asked in my new-found American accent.

'Do I get a hug from your friend?' Jamie responded, side-stepping my question. Bobby reached for him. They were about the same size, a blond boy and a striking beauty with raven-black locks. Bobby liked to show affection, and nuzzled at Jamie's cheeks and neck. Jamie blushed scarlet. A steam pipe screamed and startled us for a moment.

'They dropped me down Mount Etna,' Jamie volunteered.

'Who?'

'The Yanks of course. They can't fly a fucking kite.'

Bobby picked up Jamie's pack and we strolled from the smoky station.

'There's something big happening,' Jamie said. 'I suppose you know what I'm talking about.'

'Everyone does, for Christ's sake! You can smell it! Me and Bobby are standing by. We're with the Combined Operations force. It's right on top of us, Jamie. We don't have much time.'

There was time for a row on the boating lake at Sefton Park, a delightful spot in Toxteth, one of the most attractive and wealthy districts in the city. I liked the clean smell of Mossley Hill, the sparkling green lawns, hundreds of blue-clad soldiers recuperating on the park benches, walking sticks and crutches, pretty nurses, gorgeous flowers.

Jamie worked at the oars and the long brown boat slid gently through the lake. It seemed that his mother was expecting us, so we headed for his home when evening fell. Jamie had been here, and we'd been there, and it all sounded so foolish in the privacy of his room. Our lives were not our own. We'd wanted to be together, and it wasn't working out. He would have to fly over France and jump from a plane, machine-gun strapped to his chest. The airborne forces always went in first. Fortunately they didn't always stay, but those who returned would soon be out on another stupid mission.

'Jack and I were seventeen when we met,' Jamie said quietly. 'How old are you, Bobby?'

The boy looked lonely in his single camp bed. 'I'll soon be seventeen,' he replied.

Jamie pulled back the covers, an inviting smile on his face. 'It must be wonderful,' he said. 'You and Jack, you can go anywhere, do whatever you wish. I'm stuck with the army till the bloody war is over.'

Bobby climbed out of his cot. 'I thought you loved it,' he said.

'I do. I did. I don't know,' answered Jamie. 'I liked it when we were kids. It was exciting, a kind of new world. It's different now that I'm a sergeant.'

Bobby's lovely big dick poked through his shorts like a tent pole. They wanted each other, it was very obvious. The boy pulled his knickers down and Jamie held the swollen thing in both hands. 'Are you always like this?' he said shyly.

'Most of the time,' replied Bobby. 'Move over.'

'Don't mind me,' I said. 'I'll join in if it gets interesting.'

'You mustn't,' Jamie said. 'Don't be mean. Just hold my hand and leave us alone.'

Orgies didn't really interest me, but this was something we all wanted, a kind of love that sealed our friendship, a special intimacy that brought us much closer in a strange sort of way. Bobby was a young lion. I couldn't compete with his tremendous masculinity. There was not a jealous streak in our make-up, and it wasn't sex that bound Jamie and me together.

Jamie's fingers tightened on my hand. Bobby's happy face lit up as the exciting moment came. Jamie's lips touched mine and we ejaculated together.

There were other nights ahead, nights of tenderness and love. We picnicked in the surrounding fields, swam in the nearby pool and made the best of the time we had left.

A few days later Bobby and I reached Middlesborough and reported to the harbour master. The *El Nil* was a dirty-looking old boat. It had once belonged to King Farouk, and had served as a hospital ship among other things.

The cabins were excellent: beautiful well-built bunks and every comfort a seaman could wish for, including a settee made from fine timbers and upholstered in leather and suede. The showers were plentiful, had locks on the doors and expensive-looking fittings.

Four bunks graced our roomy cabin. Bobby had a bottom bunk, I had a bottom bunk, and the ship's cook, whose name was Hoot, slept in the bunk above my friend. Hoot had a galley boy named Jimmy, a sixteen-year-old kid who washed the pots, peeled the spuds, and did every other dirty job that came his way. He used the bunk above mine.

Jimmy was breathtakingly beautiful — wholesome, fit, masculine, slim, elegant, sun-bronzed as a young beach boy and with the grace of the pure athlete. When he smiled, strong white teeth gleamed like ivory castles. Thick, blond hair hung heavy at his well-developed neck.

The *El Nil* moved out with all the crew aboard, sailed around the coast and tied up in London at the East India docks.

'Jesus Christ!' I said to Bobby as the dockers got to work. 'I've seen these bastards work before. It takes three of the lazy bastards to load a bag of sugar and another to supervise. Look at all the fuckin' gear on the quayside. We'll be here till doomsday, kid. We'll never get loaded.'

Mountains of equipment littered the dockside — trucks, guns, case upon case of high explosives and ammunition. Ships as far as the eye could see, and a handful of dockers smoking and drinking tea.

The dockers rolled their sleeves up and I almost had a fit. Someone must have slipped whizz in their tea, or perhaps these particular guys were not members of the union. Anyway, they worked like crazy, and before long the ship was loaded to danger point.

The *El Nil* was only a 7,000-tonner, but the amount of gear she carried was staggering. All kinds of frightened young soldiers packed the ship from stem to stern; young Jimmy fed them hot coffee and Hoot's special tab-nabs.

Aircraft flew over in the sky that night and I knew it was Jamie and Clithero.

'So long, kid!' I waved at the unseen aircraft. 'Good luck, lads!'

Vera Lynn, the forces' sweetheart, was on the air, belting out a tune called 'It's A Lovely Day Tomorrow'. Everyone adored her, a real flagwaver, a lovely English rose. Even the Germans liked her. It was the sixth of June, swirling fog, the early morning mist, a cold one for the time of year. Suddenly a tremendous flash lit up the skies, and a cargo ship exploded on the horizon. The world seemed to follow in fantastic sound waves, dreadful smoke and terrifying flames.

The wind came out and chased away the fog. The greatest armada in history floated on the seas and in the air: four thousand ships and nine thousand aircraft. Hundreds of small invasion barges came into view and began to circle the vessels. Shore batteries opened up and sent shells into the blue-green waters; white spume shot into the heavens. Thousands of planes droned overhead and flattened the distant countryside.

The troops began to stir themselves. The card players called a halt, gathered up the pasteboards and pocketed the cash. Jimmy Smith made buckets of tea. The soldiers dipped their mugs in the steaming liquid and smiled gratefully at the handsome lad.

White-faced and tense, the boys climbed over the side and swung down the scrambling nets. Flat-bottomed vessels and floating rafts came alongside and busy young men unloaded the trucks, the ammunition and all the frightening instruments of death and destruction imaginable.

Bodies floated into view, dead American boys with USA printed on their backs. We saw no British dead — perhaps it was because the Americans wore life-preservers to keep them afloat. Bobby and Jim hooked them in, removed the dog-tags and watched them move off, tender young faces in the salty water.

It was an aqua carnival in full swing — ships in line, boats a-circling, gigantic lorries teetering dangerously at the boards. It was all happening and we were getting away with it. The moon and stars came out to play, the mate ordered the scrambling nets up, and the rusty old anchor chain rattled in the locker.

London was only a few hours away, the same old town, dockland bursting with military equipment and crammed with weary soldiers. Yankee troops piled aboard the *El Nil*, gum-chewing boys with sweet faces and lovely white teeth, brigands dressed to kill.

Back to the beaches, Juno and Arromanches, flame-throwers and jeeps all over the dirty decks, vomit in the scuppers, K rations and empty beer cans, the first canned beer I'd ever seen. Catholic boys moved their lips and passed the rosary through their nervous fingers. Some guys smoked a last cigarette, others just stared into space, waiting, waiting, bodies taut and tense.

Invasion barges gathered around and all the fine young warriors went down the scrambling nets, chests garlanded with hand-grenades and smoke bombs, ropes of steel-tipped bullets, breathing masks and gas goggles. Some wore shovels on their backs, entrenching tools to dig a foxhole or a grave, depending on a guy's good fortune.

Who started this madness, and why? No one asked the question! It went on and on and it was going to last forever. All the world's most beautiful young men were burning each other alive, tearing legs and heads from living creatures, destroying, mutilating. They used a jellied petrol in the flame-throwers which turned young men into orange and yellow fireballs. Some lads lined the pathways with anti-personnel mines, lightweight booby traps designed to rip the lower parts from other fine young men. They used sticky bombs and land-mines and satchels full of TNT. They tore each other's limbs with shards of bright blue steel, burned each other's eyes out. Why? They didn't even know one another, except from what they'd read in the papers and heard on the radio networks. Who wrote it up and who did the broadcasting? And why?

Thousands of troops and tons of equipment piled up on the beaches and, after a never-ending week of madness, things began to settle down. The Channel trips became less frequent, a little time to spend in dockland
and a few days off to look around.

There's something about the East End of London, the spawning grounds, the city's pulse, the heartbeat of the great metropolis. We wandered into the Railway Tavern, an off-beat pub with a three-piece band, piano and drums, singers lining up to give a turn.

'They're all queer,' said Bobby. 'Look at them. Some of them are dressed as women. Let's piss off. This place makes me nervous.' We stuck around and enjoyed the entertainment but the situation was unreal, false. It seemed a mild sort of madness and something we would never understand.

There were other pubs, lively joints where the East Enders had a knees-up every night of the week, but most of them finished up with some kind of female impersonator at the mike. That's the way they seemed to like it, so we passed them by and took a bus to the West End, a different London altogether.

The West End had a distinct vitality all its own, sidewalks packed with young people in uniform, bustling, laughing, living it up. The statue of Eros was covered in sandbags and hidden behind a blue wooden screen. Piccadilly Circus was called Rainbow Corner, headquarters of the United States forces. This is where it all happened — bodies for sale, a flourishing black market, cameras, guns, fake passports and home-made ration coupons. Street-walkers, rent boys, deserters from every army in the world gathered on Rainbow Corner and throughout the West End. It was intoxicating, addictive, a fascinating drug with an all-time high, a terrific hit and no side-effects.

The Regent Palace hotel drew us like a magnet, coffee served on a silver tray for a shilling, breathtaking rooms for a pound note, gleaming cocktail bars and the most colourful characters in Europe.

Gangsters and villains slept all day and filled the Coventry Street Corner House all through the night. Prostitutes, known as old brass nails, raised their stylish skirts and injected dope quite openly, with booze, bums and nosy parkers all around. Guys like me and Bobby, servicemen in town for the night, along with army trotters, the criminal name for deserters, spent many late nights in the Corner House just to observe the crazy antics of the gangsters and their girls at play.

The government called it a crime wave. Prison governors put three men into cells designed for one. More prisons were demanded by the growing army of reformers. Politicians said they'd build more jails, engage more policemen, reduce the crime rate and improve conditions for the long-suffering public. The papers played it down and made daily jokes about the ever increasing gangs of villains. They called them spivs and gave Joe Public something to smile about.

One night, a plane flew over dockland and was picked up by the brilliant searchlight beams. Anti-aircraft guns set the heavens alight but the pilot never even changed course.

'He must be crazy!' shouted one member of the crew.

'He's on fire!' said another. 'Why doesn't the silly bastard bail out?'

Suddenly the flaming aircraft changed direction and dived straight down on dockland.

'Jesus!' exclaimed the mate. 'They're sending suicide pilots over.'

It was the first flying bomb, the start of the terrifying rocket raids on London. We read about them in the *Daily Liar* next morning. There was panic in the streets. Frightened Londoners got their gas masks down from the attic and lived in terror once again.

Petrol and aviation fuel were in great demand by the invading forces on the continent. The harbour master transferred me and Bobby to an American tanker, a flat-bottomed vessel specially designed to scrape over the sunken ships in the harbours, not an easy task for the everyday tanker. The ship was called the *Salt Flats* and we had to join her at the Shell depot off the Isle of Wight.

Fortunately, the crew of the *Salt Flats* were a happy bunch of beer-swilling Americans. Bobby and I fitted in perfectly and soon became quite Americanised, a couple of Liverpool Yanks.

In and out of Ostend we sailed, the powerful fumes of high octane in our nostrils, jazzy music in our ears. It took nine hours to siphon out the vessel and we spent the time drinking chug-a-lug with our shipmates in the bars and *estaminets* of Belgium.

It didn't last long. Someone was making millions out of petrol. I'm sure the big oil companies didn't give it away without a huge profit. When they discovered a more economical way to shift the precious fuel, our trips ceased and the octane was supplied by a pipeline under the Channel. Farewell Shell Haven, and howdo Blackpool!

Jamie, big Duffy and handsome Jackie Clithero returned from France and held a little reunion at the Eagle and Child, a rowdy alehouse on the Huyton and Prescot road. With bonny Bobby at my side, we joined in and had a helluva time.

The war was going nicely, thousands of innocent Germans blasted to hell, women and children, dogs and cats and all living creatures. Nothing could withstand the dreadful onslaught. British and Yanks and fine young warriors from all over died like flies but it went on and on like it was never going to end.

Bobby and I strolled down town and joined a ship called the *Empire Pride*. It was a big one. God knows how many troops she carried, and like Buck said, 'He ain't gonna snitch.' Buck was my assistant, and I was the chief night troop cook.

There weren't enough hours in the day to cook all the food, so the meats were cooked by night. An escalator carried the hot meat down to the butcher's and when it was sliced, brought it back again to be served cold with a splash of hot gravy. While these operations took place, we produced breakfast — the usual stuff, sausage and tomato, bacon and egg, a couple of hundred gallons of porridge and a few pots of tea.

I think we even invented the tea bag! One of my assistants climbed the ladder to the 'tea pot', threw in a pillow-case full of tea, half a sack of sugar, and a case full of tinned milk — case, tins, labels and all! It was the only way: the lid was removed from the case and the tins struck with the sharp edge of a cleaver. We had no time to open them, and the pink and yellow labels gave the beverage a nice healthy colour...

The porridge is best forgotten about. As for the kippers, they went into a giant steam press and the fragile kipper boxes disintegrated. When the breakfast cooks came on duty, they just had to watch out for the nails.

Now when a guy works by night, his cabin is empty. Fatso, an Italian-American, wanted our cabins. 'How you guys gonna fry all dem eggs?' he approached us on our second night, fat belly wobbling like a jelly.

'Sunny side up. What's it to you?'

'You wanna hand? I'm a chef...and boy, can I fry eggs!'

Thats's the way it was: Fatso, myself, Buck, and a skinny guy with no name cracked eggs but Fatso was a smartass as well as a cook.

'The guys wanna play poker an' run a crap game in your cabin,' he said. 'You get a dollar outa the pot, and boy, there's a lotta pots in an all-night poker school!'

There were a lotta guys, too! They wanted eats and we supplied.

'Steak and chips, a dollar a throw! Can do?' asked Fatso.

'Sure. We can supply all the steaks you want but we ain't got time to cook 'em,' replied my mate.

So Fatso cooked the steak and chips, threw in a couple of eggs on the side and we were in business. Young Bobby supplied the steak, although I didn't see much of him, which was kind of sad. Fatso was too fat, Buck was an ordinary joe, and Skinny was too skinny...

Each morning, we cleared out the poker-playing Yanks and, 'according to Hoyle', picked up our chips or in this case dollar bills.

Eventually Oran loomed up on the starboard quarter and the smell of camel dung and whores filled the nostrils. A lot of Americans went ashore and set off for places unknown, but fortunately Fatso stayed aboard. Bobby and I wanted to get ashore, sleep in a hotel and make love. Buck, however, wouldn't leave us and wanted to take us to a brothel. He was a good mate, so we could hardly say no. We agreed and planned to sleep together anyway.

The brothel we chose had a bad reputation unfortunately, and during the night it got raided by MPs. As it was out of bounds to Allied personnel, getting caught meant a night in the jailhouse. We were lucky. The 'bint' (as she was called) woke us up, and Bobby and I went over the rooftops with hardly a chance of a kiss.

We dressed on a nearby flat-topped roof. While busily pulling our pants on we were joined by Buck along with the ship's baker, a grizzle-headed, middle-aged man with a hankering for whores and VD.

We got hopelessly lost in the narrow Arab streets, and discovered we were being followed.

'We're in dead trouble now,' said Grizzly. 'These bastards have got knives, and this is a fuckin' dead end. Fuckin' hell! I've got a year's back pay in my pockets!'

'What we gonna do?' asked Buck, his back to the wall and fists raised.

'Shit or bust!' I said, and pulled the automatic.

Buck thought I was fooling, but there was nothing else for it! Once you pull a gun you've got to use it. The first guy went down, and another went backwards through a door, taking it off its hinges. Ten rounds a second soon empties a magazine, and fortunately for us, emptied the narrow street too.

Poor Bobby! We couldn't even hold hands as we ran to the safety of the city lights.

Oran: tangerines, pickpockets, beautiful dark-eyed Arab boys and a harbour full of sunken ships...au revoir!

We set sail for Toulon with a shipload of Foreign Legion guys. They were a hard, restless bunch of men — tough, sexy and silent. Chests decorated with campaign ribbons, they strolled the decks, mouths watering at the sight of gorgeous American fruit and bare-chested sailor boys. If the Yanks hadn't turned my cabin into a gambling den, the Legion would have turned it into something else. Being awake all night is quite an eye-opener, and when I saw the sadness in the eyes of these silent men, I felt quite moved. No doubt about it — legionnaires were a race apart.

On and on went the good ship Lollipop: Toulon, Marseilles, Oran and round again in a kind of taxi service, dropping off troops and switching them round like a lunatic was at work in the high command.

The ship moved on to Napoli, and we called again on Mario. He was very wealthy by this time, and up to his neck in black market deals. Nothing else had changed and the old familiar cries still rang in our ears.

Mario greeted us like long lost brothers, offering us our old room in the albergo and taking us out for dinner. While we were sampling a particularly rich *marsala al uovo*, I mentioned the fact that I'd run out of ammunition. It was just off the cuff and I didn't think he'd have access to any, but I'd tried almost everyone I knew and the only stuff available was nine millimetre.

'You ever use dat ting?' he asked, topping up our glasses with the sweet Sicilian wine.

'Only when I have to...there's some naughty boys about these days.'

'You any good wid it?'

'That's a stupid question, Mario. Nobody's any good with a hand gun. I'd stand on the opposite pavement and let you shoot at me. A pistol is the most inaccurate and unreliable weapon in the world but it's good for frighteners, and if the target is only a few feet away, then I'd say...accurate.'

No doubt it was this conversation that started me on the road to crime. Mario needed someone with an English accent to sit with one of his drivers, wear a British Service Corps uniform and carry the necessary documents in the event of the vehicle being stopped.

It was quite simple really. The driver was an American deserter but correctly dressed as an RASC corporal. Together we delivered an army lorry packed with black market goods to a small town in the mountains, left it in the capable hands of the mayor and returned to Naples by bus. It just escalated from there and I made a few more trips without anything particularly exciting taking place. The money was good, considering I'd donated nothing more than my mere presence, and I enjoyed the trips.

Up and down the Mediterranean we continued. Taking advantage of the exchange rates, we changed dollars for Vichy francs, francs for lire, lire back into dollars and round again, making a profit on every deal.

Then a bad trip in the mountains scared me off. Thousands of American deserters roamed Italy at the time, and hold-ups, post office raids in broad daylight and bank robberies were daily occurrences. The black market was the only way, and hijacking the order of the day.

Realising this, Mario had supplied Sten guns: a special 'throw-away' weapon designed by some greedy arms manufacturer. They got so hot that they became useless after a few days' wear, when they were replaced by plenty more, probably made out of crushed coca-cola tins and iron piping. However, they were accurate enough if you used them hosepipe style and had asbestos fingers. My co-driver called them grease guns and told me the kids in New York made similar ones themselves.

Our load on this occasion was arms, ammunition, hand grenades and blankets. Destination: Eddie Shay, ex-member of the Long Range Desert Group and a self-styled leader who acted as mayor to one of the mountain townships. He was a real nutcase as well as a deserter, but that's Eddie's story...if he ever tells it.

On this occasion a fallen tree lay across the road. Zippo, my New York partner, said, 'This is where it all happens, kid.' With that, he pulled the pin from a hand grenade and waited.

I almost burst out laughing when a big black Yank said, 'Grab a handful of sky, you bastards!' I simply could not believe the words, and grabbed the grease gun as Zippo let fly with the grenade.

The spent cartridges landed on my lap and burnt holes in my trousers, but the attempted hijack was all over in a few seconds. They just didn't have the fire power and that's what counts, tuppence ha'penny guns or not.

Eddie wined and dined us, and was just crazy enough to offer us a ride back by plane, assuring us that it was quite safe and well organised. Zippo was another head case and would have taken the offer, but I refused and hitched a ride in a Yankee jeep.

I think I'd had enough by then and Bobby was getting restless...

A quick trip along the Suez Canal followed, with camel boys waving their long dicks at us from the banks and dirty-looking goatherds squatting, striped jellabas up around their skinny waists and long sacks of testicles hanging in the dust and sand as they emptied their bowels. Through the Red sea we went, across the Indian ocean, and then tied up in Bombay.

It was dreadful! The caste system disturbed me, everybody seemed to sleep on the streets and it looked like the whole population was homeless. As we walked the foul pavements in Grant Road, I wondered what caste the 'peg boys' belonged to. No one must marry outside his caste, but who would marry a peg boy?

'You like a nice boy, sahib?'

'Piss off!'

'Very young, very clean...only two rupees...'

Was he in the merchant caste? And the boy sitting on the greasy peg...what caste was he?

Female ratbags sang little snatches of bawdy songs they'd learned from British troops, reached out with skinny brown arms from the cages they were kept in and tried to do business with any passer-by.

Buck gave me a kick on the ankle. 'Come on, Rob. Let's get outa this fuckin' hell hole...' He snapped his fingers to a passing gharri wallah and we were whisked away in the smelly horse-drawn cab to a fabulous hotel called the Taj Mahal. It was the last word in luxury, and catered to our every whim.

Buck wanted cold English beer, and I suppose he got it in his lovely private room. Bobby and I had other ideas, and settled for a tongue bath by a gorgeous boy with kohl-darkened eyes, ruby red lips and a diamond pin in his handsome nose. He said his name was Prince Bubbles, but we didn't quite believe him.

It was all over when we reached home again. Colourful flags flew from every window and the streets of Liverpool were painted red, white and blue. Hand-written signs hung from rich and poor homes alike: 'Welcome Home Billy!', 'Welcome Home Daddy!', 'Good On Yer, Paddy!' The lights were on and the beautiful young men were coming home at last. Victory celebrations spilled onto the pavements and welcome parties took place in the open streets and roads.

A whole new world! The Beveridge plan promised free medical treatment — false teeth, free specs, glass eyes, wooden legs and wheelchairs for the disabled. Step this way and cop your pork pie hats and civilian suits. It's over! Cod liver oil and free milk for expectant mothers!

There was a distinct shortage of young peple and a great hole in the British population, so the government offered a family allowance for the second and third child. More kids for the guns next time round!

The war in Japan went on for twelve more weeks, then the Americans dropped atom bombs on the civilian population. The Japanese had no atom bombs to retaliate with. Never mind. All's fair in love and war! After destroying parts of their country for all eternity, the Americans placed the Japanese high command on trial for crimes against humanity.

Bobby wanted to stay in Blackpool and manage the hotel with his mother. I wanted to go to London, see the lights of Piccadilly and be a film star or a gangster or whatever came my way.

Jamie just wanted to die. He'd been shot up in Arnhem, taken prisoner and starved to the brink of death in a Belsen type of camp. He wouldn't let me see him. His mother said he looked like a skeleton and she didn't think he would recover.

It didn't really hit me until I saw the newsreels of walking skeletons, monsters and frightening degraded people with sunken eyes, skull-like faces and crazed expressions. Jamie was one of these dreadful creatures. No wonder he didn't want me to see him.

Bobby's mother put her arms around me, kissed me and tried to comfort me, but the tears just kept falling. Bobby had grown into a fine young man, a husky, devil-may-care seafarer. He was sensitive and understood my feelings, but it was his mother who dried away the teardrops and put me to bed.

'I must see my friend,' I said in tears. 'I must.'

'Don't take Bobby with you,' she pleaded. 'I want him home with me. I don't want him to sail again, Jackie.'

Bobby was glad to be back with his mum, understood how much Jamie meant to me and said goodbye. It had all been so wonderful.

Bobby took me to the railway station. 'So long, shipmate! Give me a kiss.'

'In front of all these people?'

'Fuck 'em all!'

'That's what I say. So long, shipmate!'

Another one had grown away.

The moment I set eyes on the old grey Mersey, I longed for the roll of a ship beneath my feet. It didn't make sense; I'd only been in England a few days, and the sea was calling me back.

I had to see Jamie before I went, so I called him on the telephone. 'I'm catching the next train,' I said.

'Please don't come,' answered my old friend. 'Please don't call.'

'For Christ's sake, Jamie! I might go back to sea again and not set eyes on you for years. I'm coming round.'

'You don't understand,' Jamie pleaded. 'Give me a couple of weeks. I can't face anybody yet. Please try to understand, Jack.'

He hung up on me, so I put the phone down and booked into a hotel. When I rang back a few hours later his mother answered. 'Jamie is too distressed to talk to anyone,' she said tearfully. 'Try and be a little patient, son.'

Her friendly voice had always been a comfort to me.

'Alright,' I replied. 'I'll ring every day. Tell Jamie I'm going up to London for a couple of weeks to sort myself out. I'm giving up the sea.'

We said goodbye and I put the phone down.

'Now what?' 'Christ! I'm talking to my friggin' self.'

I wasn't used to being alone so I strolled the city streets and thought of Jamie. Maybe they'd shaved all his hair off. Maybe-...Maybe...Perhaps if it had been me...Would I want to look at me, if I was ugly? Deformed? I wanted to ring him again and say, 'Balls! I'm coming ayway!' but I lit a cigarette and tried to put all such thoughts out of my mind.

I'd often stood and stared at the stills outside Liverpool movie houses, trying to decide which cinema to enter and hoping some nice guy would pick me up. That was all so long ago, but here and now a most fascinating young soldier stood outside the Forum staring at the stills. There was something odd about him, something wrong.

'Hey kid,' I said quietly, gripping him gently by the forearm. 'You're going to get into a hell of a lot of trouble if the MPs spot you in that uniform.'

The boy looked me straight in the eye. 'Who the hell are you?' he asked. 'Why don't you mind your own business?'

'I'm nobody,' I replied in as friendly a manner as possible, 'and you ain't a fucking soldier. There's a war on. They lock people up for impersonating members of the armed forces.'

He blushed scarlet. 'How could you tell?'

'Anyone can tell,' I replied. 'Jesus! It's a wonder you haven't been knocked off! The flashes are all wrong and the badges don't make sense. Soldiers don't wear civlian shoes. Jesus! Where you from?'

'Lancashire,' answered the downhearted lad. 'I ran away from home, but I hadn't any decent clothes to travel in, so I fixed this uniform up.'

'Well, you fixed it up all wrong,' I said. 'Let's go into the movies where it's dark.'

His name turned out to be Kelly. Too young for the forces and far too adventurous to stay at home with his coal-mining father, Kelly wanted a taste of life and a job in the big city ablaze with lights. He'd already spent what little money he had so I took him back to my hotel.

He was a splendid boy, nothing showy, a simple lad really, but very attractive. His hair was close cropped, and it stood up so tight and lively, you could almost see it growing. He had the pink lips and flawless skin of an ideal teenage boy, polished and glowing with robust health. His teeth were strong and his mouth was firm. A bonny boy, neat and trim and very athletic. Kelly played rugby for his local team, and hoped to play as a professional.

His engaging smile bewitched me. I needed a friendly boy to kiss, a gentle lad to share my bed, my life, a sweet youth to hold in my arms. I wanted this beautiful adolescent, wanted to steal him and keep him all to myself.

Undressed in the privacy of the room we shared, he looked so very big and wholesome, an excited young stallion. A sound of pleasure escaped from my lips when he said, 'I've nothing to sleep in.'

'Sleep in your skin,' I replied.

Aroused and glowing, the naked boy slid into bed and right into my waiting arms.

Starved of affection and hungry for love, Kelly's soft warm lips found my mouth, and we exchanged the most friendly kisses. All the magic was there for us to share. What was it about these gorgeous young creatures, these lovely boys who aroused other boys, set their caps at other gentle youths, weaved their strange spells, a clairvoyant telepathy leading them on and on, each bending to the other's will?

Skins grew hot and bodies boiled over, and the mouth-watering kisses became tender and teasingly light. Oh! How I loved to kiss a naked teenage boy!

Then a fever came upon us. It accelerated the pulse and made the heart beat faster. Fingers buried in my shoulders, fresh young cheek at my face, Kelly held me very tight and the magic seed escaped and ran away from us. Sounds of pleasure sneaked across the shared pillow, and I knew he cared about us.

Did this artless youth have to leave me and return home? Such virgin beauties were few and far between. Would he take a chance and come away with me? I had to find out. And what about my friend, Jamie? Would he recover quickly and let me see him? Did I have to wait forever? It was all so very miserable, and I wasn't used to misery. I wanted to seduce the lovely lad I held so close, wanted to make love to him and give him a part of my body, fill my lonely days with happiness. Life had always been so wonderful and it was about to start all over again, a whole new world, a world without war and discomfort. Would Kelly fill the empty slot, the vacant place in my homosexual heart? I wanted a friendly boy to hold my hand and kiss my hungry mouth before I closed my eyes at night. It was so important: more important than life itself!

'Kelly!' Fingers in his close-cropped hair, I touched his neck with my lips. 'Don't go home,' I said. 'Stay with me.' His virile young body gave the answer. How quickly the active flesh of youth responds! The zealour and display, the ardour and eagerness of pubescent boys always astonished me.

'Be my friend,' I said. 'I want you, Kelly. Do you want me?'

'Yes,' he said, 'I do want you. I've wanted someone like you all my life.'

'Then come away with me,' I asked. 'If you're going to run away from home, run away with me! I'm going to London, we can find a place to live, a flat or a furnished apartment. There's plenty of work to be found and money to be made. I like you, Kelly. We're the same kind of people. I won't let you down. I couldn't. I'm not like that. If you find it doesn't suit you, then we can part, but I won't desert you. I won't leave you all alone in a strange city. I'll stick with you, kid, and see you on your feet. Trust me. Take a chance. I've been around and I know what I'm doing. London is the place for a couple of guys like us. It's an open city, fill your boots, fortunes to be made! I'll look after you. Come away with me, Kelly!'

He placed a finger on my lower lip. I wanted to eat him all up, and the delicious youngster knew it. There was a hunger upon us, the voracious appetite of naked youth.

'Kelly!'

He took my hands and placed one each side of his face. His eyes were so beautiful, so wide apart and innocent. We must have exchanged a score of feverish kisses before he spoke, and said, 'I love being with you.'

'Kelly, please?'

'I'm broke,' he said simply.

'Don't worry about it,' I replied. 'Let me stake you. I'm well fixed for cash.'

He squeezed my fingers. 'Okay,' he said at last. 'I'll go away with you, but I've no clothes, nothing.'

'We can buy what you need in the morning.'

There was something about the way we held each other, something very special in the firm and masculine hand clasp.

'Shake on it!' said the boy. 'It's a deal. I'll pay you back when we start work.'

Daylight found us at Roberts and Bromley, Liverpool's fashion store for smart young men about town.

'Looks expensive,' Kelly remarked.

'It's only money,' I explained. 'There's a lot of it about. You can earn a bundle when we get started.'

Casually dressed in a pair of steward's trousers and one of my white shirts, young Kelly could easily have been mistaken for a seafaring lad as we crossed the threshold of Roberts and Bromley and stepped into the waiting arms of an overdressed sales assistant.

'What can I do for you?' he beamned.

'I'd like a few things, underwear, shirts, a suit off the peg,' replied Kelly.

The assistant produced a tape measure, and led my young friend into the changing rooms. There was a remarkable display of hats and caps near the entrance, so I stood there and waited until they returned.

What a change! The boy looked so grown up and mature, but I think I preferred him in a simple shirt and pants.

'Can I try a stetson?' he enquired.

'Why not?'

He shoved his handsome face in the mirror, settled a wide-brimmed stetson on his head, twisted the front, patted the crown and fiddled about with the brim.

'What do you think?' he asked, all smiles and glowing cheeks.

'Don't like it,' I said slowly. 'Too old for you. It makes you look like a gangster.'

'Nonsense!' the salesman objected. 'He looks charming! It's perfect. All the young men are wearing stetsons.'

Kelly turned his big innocent eyes to me. 'Why don't you try one?' he asked.

'Me? No thanks!'

188

'I think you should,' remarked the assistant. 'It'll suit you. You and your brother go well together. You look so much alike.'

He seemed to know the score and understand the ways of vain young men.

Sold!

A few pound notes settled the bill. Stetsons pushed onto the back of our heads, we strolled up town, me and my good-looking boy.

There were many things to do before we caught the midday express, loose ends to tie. The army clothes had to be dumped, so Kelly bundled them up and left them in the waiting room of the military cadet force, a sort of local boy-scout army. That's where the uniform really belonged.

'What shall I tell my old man?' he asked in the post office.

'The truth,' I replied. 'Tell him the truth.'

Kelly picked up a telegram slip and spelled out the message: 'Gone to London. Will write when I've got a job and settled in.'

'Will he miss you?' I enquired.

'Who? The old man? No, fuck him. He's got the pub, his mates, the football pools. That's not for me. Come on, let's get moving. I don't want to hang around.'

There was a lust about him, a spirit in his make-up, a vigorous desire to enjoy life. He was a real boy, a fine young companion, full of vinegar and vitality bubbling over, the flame of youth in his sparkling eye.

Most youngsters object when physical contact threatens them. The actual touch of even the friendliest hand seems to disturb them, unless of course it takes place in private. Unfortunately, I had picked up the Latin habit of body contact and a warm display of my innermost feelings. My hand reached out and rested on Kelly's wrist for a moment. He smiled at me, placed a friendly arm about my shoulder and walked me into the railway station at Lime Street.

The London train was at the platform, dozens of immaculate carriages, shiny brown paint and bright gold lettering. We climbed aboard and moved along a first-class corridor, the smell of wealth in our nostrils. There was something speical about first-class travel, not the soft touch of velvet beneath the fingers, the feel of a rich red carpet beneath the feet, but the outrageous money-to-burn attitude.

'All aboard!' The station filled with white steam and smoke. 'All aboard the London-bound express!'

The guard raised his green and red flags. Doors banged and slammed. Kelly's bright young face lit up. He threw his stetson in the air, and it landed neatly in the netting of the luggage rack. He looked so fresh-faced and guileless without the silly hat. My pulse raced.

'We're moving out!' he said, an excited flush on his cheek, a momentary catch in his musical voice. I loved the sound of a sweet lad from Lancashire. 'We're on our way!' he shouted. 'Look out London, here we come!'

A piercing whistle filled the glass-domed station with noise and steam. Kelly grabbed a wide leather strap, pulled it with both hands and slammed the window shut. White steam clouds licked at the glass, and we moved along the gleaming track, gathering speed, belting along, out into the brave new world to see what life was all about.

If you've enjoyed this book, and haven't yet read the story of Jack Robinson's childhood, this is now back in print:

Teardrops On My Drum

Liverpool in the 1920s: still Dickensian in its poverty, a city of docklands and back alleys, barefoot kids running wild in the filthy streets, bizarre eccentrics and sectarian violence. This is the world marvellously evoked by Jack Robinson in the story of his boyhood: forced to fend for himself from the earliest age, searching the city for adventure, love and sex, and joining the army as a 14-year-old boy soldier.

   'A fascinating autobiography with its evocative descriptions of life in the Liverpool of the 1920s' *(Time Out).*
ISBN 0-85449-003-5   176pp   £4.95

GMP books can be ordered from any bookshop in the UK, and from specialised bookshops overseas. If you prefer to order by mail, please send full retail price plus £1.00 for postage and packing to GMP Publishers Ltd (M.O.), P O Box 247, London N15 6RW. (For Access/Eurocard/Mastercharge give number and signature.) Comprehensive mail-order catalogue free on request.

In North America order form Alyson Publications Inc., 40 Plympton St, Boston, MA 02118, USA.

****

PLEASE SEND MAIL-ORDER CATALOGUE TO:

Name ....

Address ....

....

....

....